ELEMENTARY VECTOR ALGEBRA

ELEMENTARY VECTOR ALGEBRA

BY

A. M. MACBEATH
PROFESSOR OF MATHEMATICS
UNIVERSITY OF BIRMINGHAM

SECOND EDITION

OXFORD UNIVERSITY PRESS

Oxford University Press, Ely House, London W.1

GLASGOW NEW YORK TORONTO MELBOURNE WELLINGTON
CAPE TOWN SALISBURY IBADAN NAIROBI DAR ES SALAAM LUSAKA ADDIS ABABA
BOMBAY CALCUTTA MADRAS KARACHI LAHORE DACCA
KUALA LUMPUR SINGAPORE HONG KONG TOKYO

First Edition 1964
Second Edition 1966
Reprinted (with corrections) 1967, 1970

Printed in Great Britain by Butler & Tanner Ltd, Frome and London

PREFACE

The aim of this little book is not to prepare the reader for any specific examination, but to provide an introduction to vector algebra for those who know nothing about it and wish to learn. The approach is geometrical and non-axiomatic, intuitively acceptable properties of three-dimensional euclidean space being assumed without proof and sometimes even without explicit statement. Apart from this intentional omission, I have tried to make the treatment fairly thorough.

It is hoped that a good average pupil could master most of the material without assistance from a teacher or a lecturer. Many of the exercises are suitable for an average student who has studied the text carefully, if he is willing to spend a bit of time and effort. A few more difficult exercises have been included because of their intrinsic interest.

The book contains no mechanics, because there are plenty of good textbooks now available which deal with the subject from a vectorial point of view. However, I have of course tried to present the material in such a way that readers will be able to apply the methods both in mechanics and in geometry. Algebraic ideas and terms (like 'distributive' and 'commutative') are introduced so as to prepare the student for a later study of abstract algebra, of which vector algebra is a part.

The usefulness of the vector method in solid analytical geometry still seems not to have been fully appreciated. It helps to develop three-dimensional intuition and to unify algebraic and geometrical concepts. Lecturing on the subject has led me to introduce the terms 'direction vector' of a line and 'normal vector' of a plane, instead of the direction cosines of other writers. This seems to be a logical change, and I hope that it will be generally accepted.

A fair amount of emphasis is laid on explicit work with coordinates and components, because this seems to reassure students who are unhappy with too much abstraction. It is a mistake to imagine that vectors can completely replace cartesian methods, though they greatly assist understanding, particularly in dealing with the plane and the straight line in solid coordinate geometry.

I have restricted myself to this easy part of the subject, where the vector method is most clearly relevant.

The absolute value sign is used to denote the length of a vector and **x** is chosen instead of **r** for a typical position vector. These notations are not yet standard, but the first is usual in the theory of higher dimensional space and the second is more consistent with the use of x, y, z for coordinates. Generally speaking, the aim has been to give a firm basis for further work, so that the minimum of 'unlearning' will be needed, whether the reader goes on to study applied mathematics, abstract algebra or functional analysis.

A first draft of parts of the book was circulated in cyclostyled form to students at Queen's College, Dundee. I should like to thank some of them for helpful comments. I should also like to thank Dr. Iain Adamson and Mr. Henry Jack for several constructive criticisms.

A. M. M.

1963

CONTENTS

1

MATHEMATICAL NOTATION

To understand this book one must be willing to alter one's ideas about the use of symbols in mathematics. Hitherto, for most readers, symbols have denoted only numbers or points, but now they will be used to denote other things as well. This extension of their use is desirable because symbols help to achieve economy and precision. It is easy to forget how much one gains by their use. For instance, a simple formula like '$a^2-b^2 = (a-b)(a+b)$' becomes much more complicated when stated in words: 'The difference of the squares of two numbers is the product of their difference and their sum.' The verbal statement is longer and less precise, for it is not clear whether the difference referred to is $a-b$ or $b-a$; and if a more complicated formula had been chosen, it would very probably have been impossible to put it adequately into words at all. A wider use of symbols to include other things besides points and numbers can be expected to lead to further simplifications.

The algebra of vectors, with which we deal in this book, arose naturally out of the attempt to apply symbolic methods in certain parts of geometry and mechanics. A vector is a combined *number-direction*, not merely a magnitude but a magnitude associated with a direction in space. For instance, the velocity of a moving particle is not specified simply by answering the question *how fast* the particle is travelling, but one must also know *in what direction* it is moving. Thus a force is required to keep a body moving uniformly in a circular path. Though the speed is constant, the direction of motion does not remain the same, so the velocity is continually changing. A force, tending to move a body from its steady uniform motion, can also be represented by a vector. To understand the action of the force one must know not only how strongly it is tending to move the body, but one must know too in what direction it is tending to move it. As well as these applications in physics, vectors have an application in geometry which will be explained in the next chapter and which forms the main topic of this book.

In addition to symbols which denote objects, there are symbols, such as $+$, $-$, $\times$, $.$, which are used to express various processes or *operations* performed on the objects. Thus $a+b$ denotes the result of the operation of adding the two numbers a, b. Some operations may be expressed without using an operation symbol at all, like the product ab or the line PQ. Brackets are another important type of symbol. They do not themselves denote operations, but indicate the order in which the operations are to be carried out. Thus $(a \times b)+c$ denotes the result of two operations: 'Multiply the number a by the number b and add c to the result.' The expression $a \times (b+c)$ is the same as the other except for the position of the brackets, yet it means something quite different: 'Add b to c and multiply a by the result.' In the first instance the brackets would normally be left out because, by convention, multiplication takes priority over addition if there are no brackets. However, if there are two or more symbols of operation in the same expression, brackets are necessary unless some special reason allows them to be left out. The role of brackets in vector algebra, and indeed in the whole of mathematics, is essentially the same as in number algebra, and the rules governing their use are the same.

Ordinary usage assigns a meaning to the symbols $+$, $-$, $\times$, $.$, when these are associated with numbers. If $\mathbf{a}$, $\mathbf{b}$ are vectors, however, no meaning has been attached to the expressions $\mathbf{a}+\mathbf{b}$, $\mathbf{a}\times\mathbf{b}$, $\mathbf{a}.\mathbf{b}$, and we are free to give them any meaning we please. The meaning that is always given to the $+$ sign in vector algebra is connected with the applications in physics. The well-known 'triangle of forces' and 'triangle of velocities' express the fact that forces and velocities combine according to the law of vector addition.

It might seem better to use a completely new symbol for vector addition and so avoid confusion with the addition of numbers. However, if different symbols were invented for every possible operation, the total number of symbols would have to be very large. One reason for using the $+$ sign for the composition of vectors is simply the need for economy in the number of symbols. Another reason will be given in a moment.

We all know that if a and b are numbers, then $a+b = b+a$. In the next chapter a similar result will be found for vectors: if $\mathbf{a}$ and $\mathbf{b}$ are two vectors, then $\mathbf{a}+\mathbf{b} = \mathbf{b}+\mathbf{a}$. Why does this require discussion? Is it not obvious? To understand the answer, one must remember that there is, *a priori*, no logical connexion between the $+$ of vector algebra and the $+$ of number-algebra. Vector addition is another use of the symbol $+$, and the two kinds of addition are *different operations with the same name.* If, knowing that $a+b = b+a$ for numbers, we conclude that the same is true for vectors, our logic is hopelessly faulty. It is as if there were two people called Smith, and we conclude that, because one of them has fair hair, the other must have fair hair also. To discover the colour of one person's hair, we do not look at somebody else's, even if their names are the same. Similarly, if we want to know how vectors behave when they are added, it is no use considering numbers, with their quite different addition. We have to examine vector addition separately, using its own geometrical definition.

It turns out that vector addition does indeed satisfy many of the formal laws of operation satisfied by number addition. This, as well as economy in the use of symbols, is another reason why the $+$ sign is used to represent it. Once one has proved the laws, habits acquired in number-algebra can usefully be transferred to vector algebra. However, even after the laws have been established, one should avoid the casual, almost mechanical attitude that many people seem to acquire in the study of elementary algebra. Every identity in vector algebra is equivalent to a geometrical theorem, sometimes quite a complicated one. For instance, the simple identity $\mathbf{a}+\mathbf{b} = \mathbf{b}+\mathbf{a}$ is equivalent to the theorem that the opposite sides of a parallelogram are equal.

As well as vector addition, three different kinds of vector multiplication will be defined later. One of these combines numbers with vectors, the other two combine vectors with one another. In ordinary algebra there are three ways of writing down the product of two numbers a and b, namely ab, $a.b$, and $a \times b$. These notations, taken over into vector algebra, denote three different kinds of multiplication: $k\mathbf{a}$ for the product of the number k and the vector $\mathbf{a}$, $\mathbf{a}.\mathbf{b}$ for one kind of product of two vectors, and $\mathbf{a} \times \mathbf{b}$ for the other kind of product of two vectors. These operation-symbols, interchangeable in number-algebra, have different meanings in vector algebra, and it is important not to confuse them. In this and in several other ways the analogy between number and vector multiplication is not so close as the analogy between the additions. Other points of difference will be noted in later chapters.

Though we shall refer to some of our discussions as 'proofs', no attempt is made to set up a rigorous deductive structure. For us 'proof' will mean a deduction from intuitively clear properties of the space in which we live. Mathematical proof, in the strict sense, means deduction from a number of basic assumptions, called axioms, which should be clearly and precisely stated. It is particularly difficult to give an axiomatic treatment of pure euclidean geometry of three dimensions, and such a discussion would be out of keeping with the rest of the material in this book. The reader who is interested in an axiomatic treatment of solid geometry should consult, for instance, *The Foundations of Geometry*, by

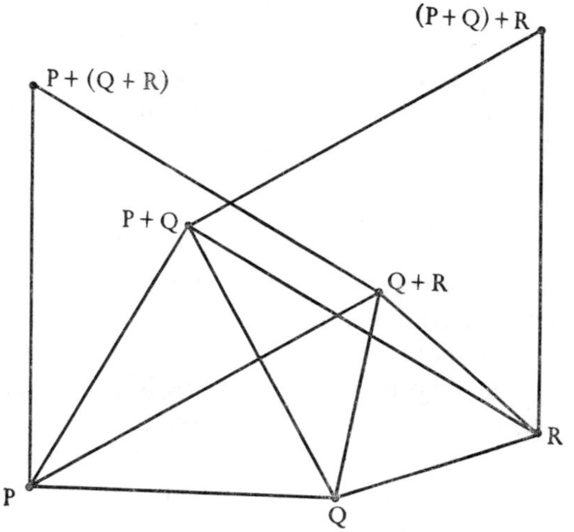

FIG. 1 'Addition of points' in the plane.

G. de B. Robinson (Toronto, 1940) and the references given on p. 162 of that book.

One way to become convinced of the need for thorough discussion of the rules in a new kind of algebra is to consider an algebra in which the rules break down. As an example we define an 'addition of points' in the plane which has some unusual properties. It is not, of course, a standard definition, but is devised merely as an illustration. Let capital letters P, Q, R, ... denote points of the plane. Let P+Q denote the third vertex of the equilateral triangle on PQ as base which is on the left side of PQ to an observer looking along PQ from P towards Q. With this definition the points P+Q, Q+P will be different, being the vertices of the two equilateral triangles on opposite sides of the base PQ. Also, if

P, Q, R are three distinct points, the points $P+(Q+R)$, $(P+Q)+R$ are different, as illustrated in Fig. 1. This means that the expression $P+Q+R$ is ambiguous, having two possible meanings which must be distinguished by the use of brackets. Though the addition just defined does not satisfy the laws satisfied by number addition, it satisfies other identities which number addition does not. For instance, the following identities hold.

$$(P+(P+(P+(P+(P+(P+Q)))))) = Q.$$
$$P+(P+(P+Q)) = (Q+P)+(P+Q).$$
$$\text{If } P+Q = R, \quad \text{then } Q+R = P.$$
$$(P+Q)+R = (P+(Q+R))+Q.$$

Of course there is no limit to the new algebras one might invent, and the one I have just described to illustrate the failure of the rules is of no importance, mathematical or otherwise. Vector algebra, on the other hand, though at first sight it may seem artificial, is important and fundamental. The reader will have to take this on trust at first because a certain amount of groundwork must be done before really interesting applications are possible. After a time, however, it will become obvious that vector algebra is the natural method for tackling problems in solid geometry. This view is not contradicted by the fact that many of these problems were done originally without vectors, since mechanics and solid geometry were well developed before vectors were invented. Problems solved for the first time in mathematics are usually done by a rather difficult method, the solution then being simplified by later work. The Greeks and Romans could, with difficulty, add and multiply numbers without having Arabic numerals, but this is no argument against using Arabic numerals today.

Once a few chapters have been mastered, the reader should take an older textbook on solid coordinate geometry and try to rewrite as many as possible of the equations in vector form. He will soon be convinced of the value of the vector notation, in which one simple equation can often replace three complicated numerical equations. It is quite possible to find oneself becoming impatient with the writer of such a book because he does not use vectors, though of course many of the equations and formulae were found long before vectors were invented. It is perhaps best to think of vectors as a suitable notation for certain mathematical problems, so suitable that no one who knew about it would dream of tackling the problems in any other way; just as no one who had to multiply two large numbers together would think of using any notation except Arabic numerals, though Roman numerals may do very well on the dial of a clock.

Another unexpected advantage of the vector method is the way in which it links up with other parts of mathematics. For instance, the vector product, as we shall see in Chapter 5, has a close connexion with the method of 'cross-multiplication' in dealing with linear homogeneous equations, and the scalar triple product, written out in terms of components, is nothing but a three by three determinant. Some parts of plane geometry and trigonometry, too, include formulae which are easily recognizable as special cases of vector equations, for instance Pythagoras's Theorem and the formula for the cosine of the difference of two angles. However, the real power of vectors becomes clear in three dimensions, as will be seen in Chapters 6 and 7 where we deal with solid coordinate geometry and spherical trigonometry. Time spent on the study of vector algebra is thus time well spent, because it helps to understand material which used to be thought to belong to several different branches of mathematics.

2

VECTOR ADDITION

1. Introduction

This chapter begins by explaining what vectors are and describing the triangle rule for vector addition. Historically, vector addition was devised in order to deal with the composition and resolution of forces and velocities. The triangle rule, or, more correctly, the triangle definition, was dictated by the triangle of velocities and the triangle of forces in mechanics. Later it became clear that vector algebra was helpful in many geometrical problems and, later still, more general vector spaces (outside the scope of this book) were invented and applied to the theory of linear equations and other parts of mathematics. Nowadays the concept of vector addition is a basic part of the equipment of any pure or applied mathematician.

Most of this first chapter and some parts of the following chapters are necessarily concerned with spade work, and the real value of the method will not be clear to the reader until later. However, a few illustrations are included to indicate how vector algebra can throw fresh light on some known geometrical situations. There are no applications to mechanics in this book, but the reader can easily find out about such applications from any modern textbook on mechanics, since vectors are now a standard method in this field.

2. Vectors

Definition 1. A non-zero vector is a combination of three things:

(1) a positive number called its *magnitude* or *length*,
(2) a direction in space,
(3) a *sense* (making more precise the idea of direction).

The direction may be described by specifying that the vector is parallel to a given line, and the sense by specifying one of the two possible directions of travel along the line. The exceptional *zero vector*, which will always be denoted by **0**, has zero magnitude, but its direction and sense are not defined. Symbols in bold type (**a**,

b, ...) will be used to denote vectors. The magnitude of the vector **a** will be denoted by | **a** |.

Two vectors are defined to be *equal* if they have the same magnitude, direction and sense. It is most important to understand that two vectors are not equal unless they are equal in all three respects—magnitude, direction and sense. Vectors should never be called equal if they are equal in magnitude only.

Let P and Q be two points of space. Then the line segment joining P to Q represents a vector whose magnitude is the distance between P and Q, whose direction is that of the line PQ and whose sense is the direction of travel from P to Q. The point P will be called the *initial point* and the point Q the *endpoint* of the segment. The vector which is represented by the segment with initial point P and endpoint Q will be denoted by $\overrightarrow{PQ}$. The vectors $\overrightarrow{PQ}$ and $\overrightarrow{QP}$ have the same magnitude and direction but *opposite sense*. Any 'degenerate' line-segment $\overrightarrow{PP}$ with the same initial and endpoint may be taken to represent the zero vector **0**.

Since two vectors with the same magnitude, direction and sense are equal, it follows that the same vector can be represented by many different line-segments. For example, if ABCD is a parallelogram, the vectors $\overrightarrow{AB}$ and $\overrightarrow{DC}$ are equal. On the other hand, if ABC is an equilateral triangle, the vectors $\overrightarrow{BC}$, $\overrightarrow{CA}$, $\overrightarrow{AB}$ are all different, since they differ in direction.

3. The sum of two vectors

The simplest of the vector operations is that of addition Because of a formal analogy with the addition of numbers the same sign + is used to represent it.

Definition 2. Let **a**, **b** be two vectors, represented by line segments OP = **a**, $\overrightarrow{PQ}$ = **b**, so that the endpoint of the segment representing **a** is the initial point of the segment representing **b**. Then the vector **a**+**b** is defined to be $\overrightarrow{OQ}$.

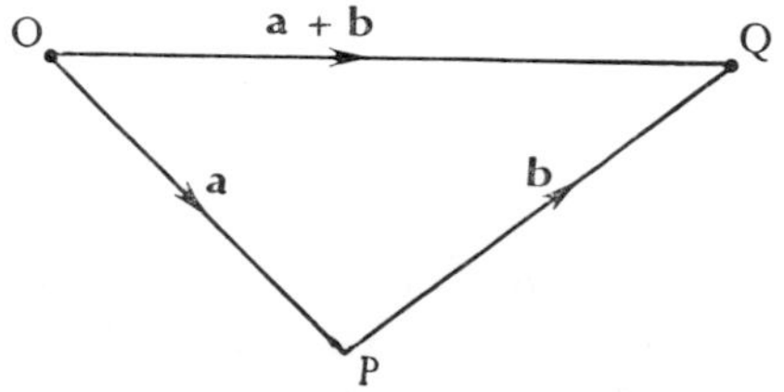

FIG. 2 Vector addition.

Definition 2 is often called the *triangle rule*, for if $\overrightarrow{OP}$, $\overrightarrow{PQ}$ are not parallel, the vectors **a**, **b**, **a**+**b** are represented by the three sides of the triangle OPQ (Fig. 2). However, the definition still has a meaning if O, P, Q do not form a triangle in the usual sense, if O, P, Q lie on a line, for instance, or when one of the vectors concerned is the zero vector and two of the points O, P, Q coincide. These possibilities require study.

Collinearity. Suppose that **a** and **b** have the same direction and sense, so that P lies between O and Q on the line OQ (Fig. 3). Then the vector $\overrightarrow{OQ} = \mathbf{a}+\mathbf{b}$ has the same direction and sense as **a** and **b**, and its magnitude is the sum of their magnitudes;

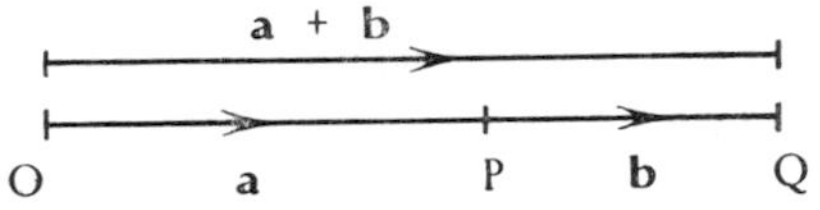

FIG. 3

$$|\mathbf{a}+\mathbf{b}| = |\mathbf{a}| + |\mathbf{b}|. \tag{1}$$

This relation holds *only if* **a**, **b** *have the same direction and sense.* In general, the sum of the lengths of two sides of a triangle is greater than the length of the third side and we have the inequality

$$|\mathbf{a}+\mathbf{b}| < |\mathbf{a}| + |\mathbf{b}|.$$

Coincidence. (i) If P and Q coincide in Definition 2, the vector $\mathbf{b} = \overrightarrow{PQ} = \overrightarrow{PP}$ is the zero vector **0**. The triangle rule then gives

$$\mathbf{a}+\mathbf{0} = \mathbf{a}. \tag{2}$$

This fits very nicely into the analogy with number-algebra.

(ii) If the point P coincides with the point O, then $\mathbf{a} = \mathbf{0}$, and we derive

$$\mathbf{0}+\mathbf{b} = \mathbf{b}.$$

Finally, if O coincides with Q, we find that

$$\overrightarrow{OP}+\overrightarrow{PO} = \mathbf{0}.$$

Thus the sum of two vectors which are equal in magnitude and direction but opposite in sense is the zero vector. The analogy with number-algebra then suggests the following definition.

Definition 3. The vector $-\mathbf{a}$, called the *negative* of **a**, is the vector which has the same magnitude and direction as **a**, but opposite sense.

With this notation, the last result can be written:

$$\mathbf{a}+(-\mathbf{a}) = \mathbf{0}. \tag{3}$$

Note also that

$$-(-\mathbf{a}) = \mathbf{a}. \tag{4}$$

4. Notes on Definition 2. The commutative law

The vectors **a, b** may be represented as sides $\overrightarrow{OP}$, $\overrightarrow{PQ}$ of many different triangles OPQ. It might appear, therefore, that Definition 2 does not lead to a unique sum. However, all such triangles OPQ are congruent and similarly placed; so the different line-segments $\overrightarrow{OQ}$ will all represent the same vector, and the sum is, in fact, unique.

The vectors **a** and **b** do not enter symmetrically into the definition, since the initial point of **b** coincides with the endpoint of **a.** To obtain the sum **b**+**a,** complete the parallelogram OPQR. Then $\overrightarrow{OR} = \mathbf{b}$, $\overrightarrow{RQ} = \mathbf{a}$, so from the triangle ORQ (Fig. 4), $\mathbf{b}+\mathbf{a} = \overrightarrow{OQ}$. This proves the identity, known as the *commutative law,*

$$\mathbf{a}+\mathbf{b} = \mathbf{b}+\mathbf{a} \tag{5}$$

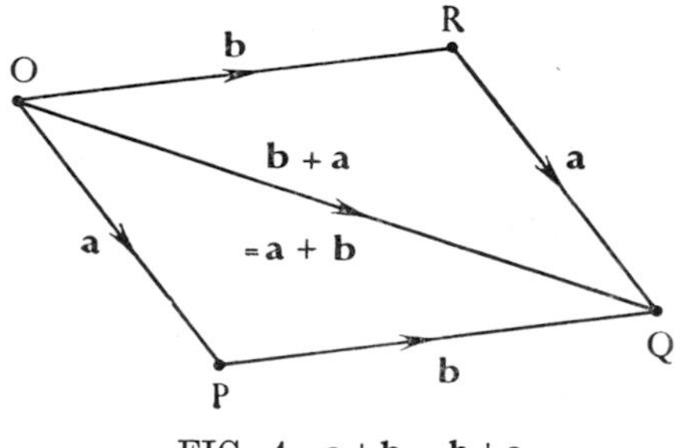

FIG. 4 $\mathbf{a}+\mathbf{b} = \mathbf{b}+\mathbf{a}$

Exercises

1. Show that, if **a, b** have the same direction but opposite sense and $|\mathbf{a}| > |\mathbf{b}|$, then **a**+**b** has the same direction and sense as **a.** What is the magnitude of **a**+**b** in this case?

2. The proof given of the commutative identity (5) is valid only when the directions of **a** and **b** are different. Consider separately the cases when

(i) **a, b** have the same direction and sense,

(ii) **a, b** have the same direction and opposite senses,
(iii) **b** is the zero vector.

5. Use of brackets. Associative law

Brackets are used in vector algebra with the same meaning as in number-algebra: the expression inside a bracket is to be treated as a single symbol for the purpose of combining with anything outside the bracket. Thus the expression

$$(\mathbf{a}+\mathbf{b})+\mathbf{c}$$

denotes the result of the following sequence of operations:

(1) evaluate the sum $\mathbf{a}+\mathbf{b}$, obtaining a vector $\mathbf{d}$,
(2) evaluate $\mathbf{d}+\mathbf{c}$.

On the other hand, the expression

$$\mathbf{a}+(\mathbf{b}+\mathbf{c})$$

is evaluated as follows:

(1) evaluate $\mathbf{b}+\mathbf{c}$ to obtain $\mathbf{e}$, say,
(2) evaluate $\mathbf{a}+\mathbf{e}$.

It does not seem at all clear that these two sequences of operations should lead to the same answer; but we shall now prove that in fact they always do. That is,

$$\mathbf{a}+(\mathbf{b}+\mathbf{c}) = (\mathbf{a}+\mathbf{b})+\mathbf{c}. \qquad (6)$$

This result is known as the *associative law* for vector addition.

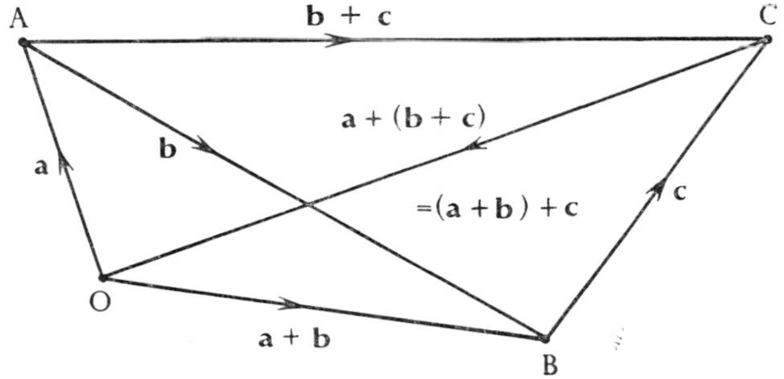

FIG. 5 $\mathbf{a}+(\mathbf{b}+\mathbf{c}) = (\mathbf{a}+\mathbf{b})+\mathbf{c}$

Proof (Fig. 5). Let the vectors **a, b, c** be represented by the line-segments $\overrightarrow{OA}$, $\overrightarrow{AB}$, $\overrightarrow{BC}$ respectively. From Definition 1, $\mathbf{a}+\mathbf{b} = \overrightarrow{OA}+\overrightarrow{AB} = \overrightarrow{OB}$, so $(\mathbf{a}+\mathbf{b})+\mathbf{c} = \overrightarrow{OB}+\overrightarrow{BC} = \overrightarrow{OC}$. Again by Definition 1,

$$\mathbf{b}+\mathbf{c} = \overrightarrow{AB}+\overrightarrow{BC} = \overrightarrow{AC}, \text{ so } \mathbf{a}+(\mathbf{b}+\mathbf{c}) = \overrightarrow{OA}+\overrightarrow{AC} = \overrightarrow{OC}.$$

Thus the processes indicated by the left and right sides of the equation both lead to the same result, the vector $\overrightarrow{OC}$.

6. The sum of a number of vectors

The associative law allows us to omit brackets without ambiguity in a sum of three vectors, the value common to the left and right sides of equation (6) being written, simply $\mathbf{a}+\mathbf{b}+\mathbf{c}$. This result can be extended to a sum of any finite number of vectors. The expression

$$\mathbf{a}_1+\mathbf{a}_2+ \dots +\mathbf{a}_n$$

have a value independent of the order in which the additions are performed.

The sum of n vectors may also be obtained directly by constructing a diagram of line-segments in which the endpoint of each segment is the initial point of the next one. The sum is represented by the segment joining the first initial point to the last endpoint. For instance, if $n = 5$ and the vectors **a, b, c, d, e** are represented by segments $\overrightarrow{OA}$, $\overrightarrow{AB}$, $\overrightarrow{BC}$, $\overrightarrow{CD}$, $\overrightarrow{DE}$, then the sum $\mathbf{a}+\mathbf{b}+\mathbf{c}+\mathbf{d}+\mathbf{e}$ is represented by the segment $\overrightarrow{OE}$ (Fig. 6).

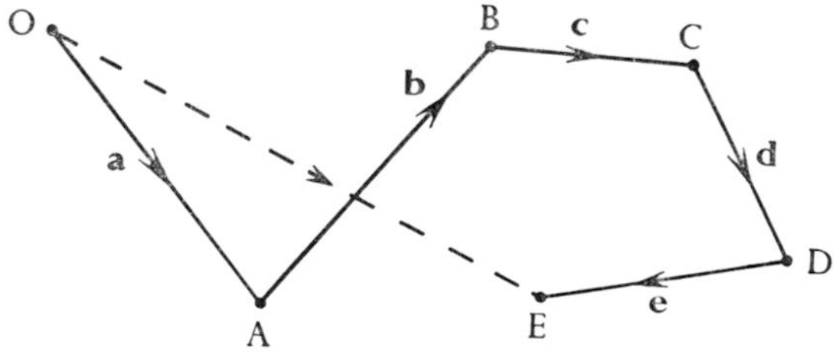

FIG. 6 The sum of a number of vectors.

7. Subtraction of vectors

Having defined the negative $-\mathbf{a}$ of a vector **a**, we define subtraction as adding the negative, that is, $\mathbf{b}-\mathbf{a} = \mathbf{b}+(-\mathbf{a})$. Subtraction is then the operation inverse to addition (as in number-algebra) and $\mathbf{x} = \mathbf{b}-\mathbf{a}$ is the unique solution of the vector equation $\mathbf{x}+\mathbf{a} = \mathbf{b}$; for the triangle OPQ with $\overrightarrow{OP} = \mathbf{x}$, $\overrightarrow{PQ} = \mathbf{a}$, $\overrightarrow{OQ} = \mathbf{b}$, represents equally the equation

$$\mathbf{x}+\mathbf{a} = \mathbf{b}(\overrightarrow{OP}+\overrightarrow{PQ} = \overrightarrow{OQ}) \text{ and } \mathbf{x} = \mathbf{b}+(-\mathbf{a})(\overrightarrow{OP} = \overrightarrow{OQ}+\overrightarrow{QP})$$

(Fig. 7).

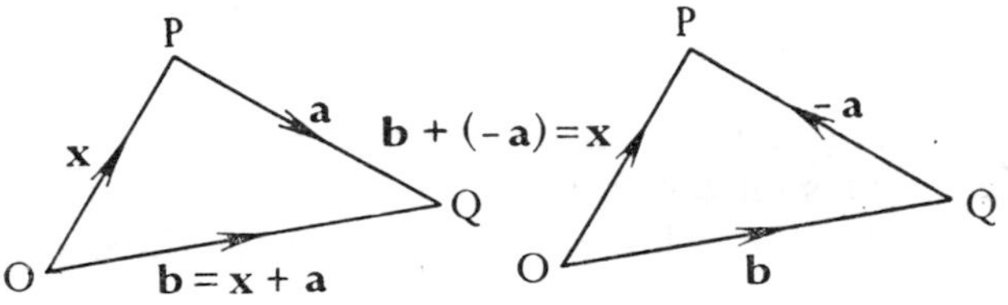

FIG. 7

We can therefore take a term from one side of a vector equation to the other, changing its sign, for this is the same thing as subtracting the term from both sides. Similarly we can change all the signs in a vector equation. For example, from the equation

$$\mathbf{a}+\mathbf{b} = \mathbf{c},$$

we deduce by adding $-\mathbf{c}-\mathbf{b}-\mathbf{a}$ to both sides, that

$$-\mathbf{c} = -\mathbf{a}-\mathbf{b}.$$

8. Geometrical illustration

It is well known that, if all the sides of a parallelogram have equal length, that is, if the parallelogram is a rhombus, then its diagonals are perpendicular. (We cannot give a vector proof of this result at present, but see Chapter 4, p. 52.) If **a** is the vector represented by one side of a parallelogram, and **b** is represented by an adjacent side, then the diagonals (with suitable choice of sense) represent $\mathbf{a}+\mathbf{b}$ and $\mathbf{a}-\mathbf{b}$. Thus the perpendicularity of the diagonals of a rhombus can be indicated, in vector language, as follows: 'If $|\mathbf{a}| = |\mathbf{b}|$, then $\mathbf{a}+\mathbf{b}$ is at right angles to $\mathbf{a}-\mathbf{b}$ (Fig. 8).

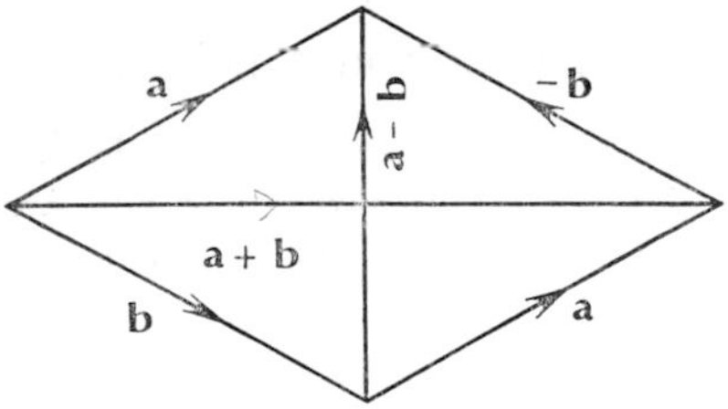

FIG. 8

Now let ABC be a triangle and let O be the centre of the circle through A, B and C, so that the vectors $\overrightarrow{OA}$, $\overrightarrow{OB}$, $\overrightarrow{OC}$ are all equal in length. Denote these vectors, for shortness, by **a**, **b** and **c**. Let H be the point defined by the vector equation $\overrightarrow{OH} = \mathbf{a}+\mathbf{b}+\mathbf{c}$. Then from the triangle COH,

$$\overrightarrow{CH} = \overrightarrow{CO}+\overrightarrow{OH} = -\mathbf{c}+\mathbf{a}+\mathbf{b}+\mathbf{c} = \mathbf{a}+\mathbf{b}.$$

Again, $$\overrightarrow{BA} = \overrightarrow{BO}+\overrightarrow{OA} = -\mathbf{b}+\mathbf{a} = \mathbf{a}-\mathbf{b}.$$

But now, $|\mathbf{a}| = |\mathbf{b}|$, so by the result about the rhombus, $\overrightarrow{CH}$ and $\overrightarrow{BA}$ are at right angles, that is H lies on the altitude through C. By symmetry, H lies also on the other two altitudes. This proves again the well-known result that the three altitudes of

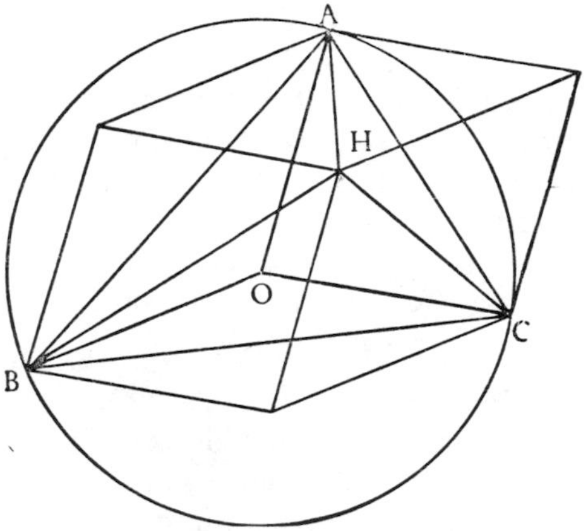

FIG. 9

a triangle meet at a point H (the orthocentre). In addition, we have obtained the vector relation $\overrightarrow{OH} = \overrightarrow{OA}+\overrightarrow{OB}+\overrightarrow{OC}$.

The proof just given of the orthocentre property depends only on the associative law, enabling us to omit brackets in the sums, the commutative law, concealed in the phrase 'by symmetry', and the fact that the diagonals of a rhombus are perpendicular. The proof is therefore equivalent to a simple geometrical proof, and one might be tempted to think that the vector algebra is not essential. In a sense it is not absolutely essential, but the geometrical construction required if one is to do without vectors is surprisingly complicated, as one can see from Fig. 9, where all the parallelograms are drawn in. Once this construction has been made, the geometrical proof is not difficult, and readers who feel unsure of the vector algebra (quite a natural feeling at this stage) may find that it helps to study this figure. They are bound to agree, though, that the vector proof is better.

9. Multiplication of a vector by a number

Sometimes the same vector may occur twice or more often in the same sum as in the expression (Fig. 10)

$$\mathbf{a}+\mathbf{a}+\mathbf{a}+\mathbf{b}+\mathbf{b}.$$

It is natural to write this in the shorter form

$$3\mathbf{a}+2\mathbf{b},$$

as in number algebra.

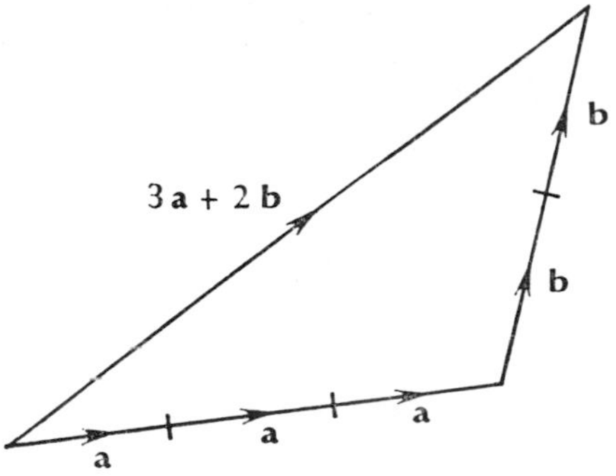

FIG. 10

Similarly $(-3)\mathbf{a}$ would naturally denote the sum $-\mathbf{a}-\mathbf{a}-\mathbf{a}$. We are thus led to the idea of multiplying a vector by a positive or negative whole number.

Now consider the magnitude, direction and sense of the vectors $3\mathbf{a}$, $2\mathbf{a}$, ... , $-\mathbf{a}$, $(-2)\mathbf{a}$, ... Leaving aside the exceptional case $\mathbf{a} = \mathbf{0}$, we may consider $\mathbf{a}$ to be the vector represented by the segment $\overrightarrow{OP}$, where O, P are distinct points. Continue the line OP in both directions, and mark on this line a sequence of points P_2, P_3, P_4, ... spaced at equal distances $|OP|$ beyond P, and another sequence of points P_{-1}, P_{-2}, ... spaced at equal distances $|OP|$ beyond O. The segments $\overrightarrow{PP_2}$, $\overrightarrow{P_2P_3}$, &c., equal in magnitude, direction and sense to $\overrightarrow{OP}$, all represent the same vector $\mathbf{a}$.

From the definition of vector addition,

$$\begin{aligned}\overrightarrow{OP_m} &= \overrightarrow{OP}+\overrightarrow{PP_2}+ \dots +\overrightarrow{P_{m-1}P_m}\\ &= \mathbf{a}+\mathbf{a}+ \dots +\mathbf{a} \quad (m \text{ times})\\ &= m\mathbf{a}.\end{aligned}$$

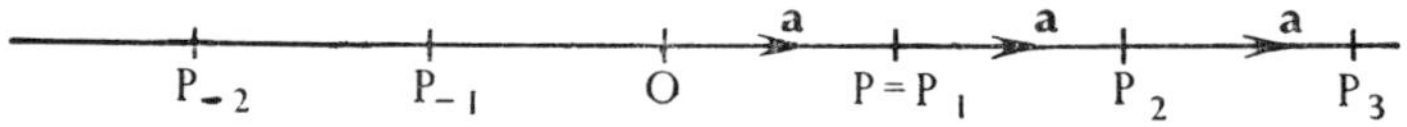

FIG. 11

Thus if m is a positive whole number, $m\mathbf{a}$ is the vector with the same direction and sense as $\mathbf{a}$, but with m times the magnitude.

Similarly, $(-m)\mathbf{a}$, represented by the segment OP_{-m}, is the vector with the same direction as $\mathbf{a}$, opposite sense and m times the magnitude. This all suggests the following definition in which the multipliers *need not be whole numbers*.

Definition 4a. Let $\mathbf{a}$ be a non-zero vector and k a non-zero number. The vector $k\mathbf{a}$ is defined by the following rules, giving, in order, its magnitude, direction, and sense.

(1) $|k\mathbf{a}| = |k|\,|\mathbf{a}|$,

(2) Direction of $k\mathbf{a}$ = direction of $\mathbf{a}$,

(3) Sense of $k\mathbf{a}$ and $\mathbf{a}$ are the same if k is positive, opposite if k is negative.

This definition does not allow the zero vector or the number zero to occur in a product. The obvious value for such products is the zero vector (for many reasons). Hence

Definition 4b. The product of any number and the zero vector is the zero vector. The product of the number zero and any vector is the zero vector. That is, $0\mathbf{a} = k\mathbf{0} = \mathbf{0}$.

Note. Definition 4 may seem a little cumbersome by comparison with the simple idea of repeated addition of a vector to itself mentioned at the beginning of this section. However, the simpler idea is unsuitable as a definition because it only describes multiplication by a positive or negative *integer*, and it is convenient to attach a meaning to expressions like $\sqrt{2}\mathbf{a}$, or $\frac{5}{8}\mathbf{a}$, which cannot be defined by successive addition.

10. The distributive laws

In this section we prove the following identities, known as *distributive laws*. The last of these laws enables us to omit brackets in the expression $kl\mathbf{a}$, which would otherwise be ambiguous. In this it resembles the associative law (6).

$$(k+l)\mathbf{a} = k\mathbf{a}+l\mathbf{a}. \tag{7}$$

$$k(\mathbf{a}+\mathbf{b}) = k\mathbf{a}+k\mathbf{b}. \tag{8}$$

$$k(l\mathbf{a}) = (kl)\mathbf{a}. \tag{9}$$

It will be noticed that the proof of (7) is split up to cover rather a large number of particular cases, according to the sign and relative magnitude of the numbers k, l. The situation, geometrically, is that of three points A, B, C on a line, and there are six possible orders, reading from left to right, in which they can be arranged (neglecting the possibility that two of them might coincide). Though it is rather tiresome to have to consider all these cases in the proof, it is a great advantage of the distributive law that it does, in fact, cover all cases, and once the law is established it can be applied automatically, without any worry about drawing diagrams of different cases (sometimes without drawing a diagram at all). A good instance of this occurs in § 13 of this chapter, dealing with the point dividing a segment in a given ratio, the same formula covering points of subdivision both inside and outside the segment.

Case (1) in the proof of (7), when k and l are both positive, is, in a sense, the fundamental one, since the other cases are deduced from it by taking terms across from one side to the other of equations. The reader may find it interesting to give direct proofs of Cases 2 to 6, drawing a diagram for each case.

Proof of (7). Case (1). Suppose that $k > 0$, $l > 0$, $\mathbf{a} \neq \mathbf{0}$. The vectors $k\mathbf{a}$, $l\mathbf{a}$ then have the same direction and sense—that of $\mathbf{a}$—so by formula (1), § 2, the magnitude of their sum is

$$|\,k\mathbf{a}\,| + |\,l\mathbf{a}\,| = |\,k\,|\,|\,\mathbf{a}\,| + |\,l\,|\,|\,\mathbf{a}\,| = (k+l)\,|\,\mathbf{a}\,|.$$

Now $k+l$ is a positive number, so the vector $(k+l)\mathbf{a}$ has the same direction and sense as $\mathbf{a}$, and its magnitude is $(k+l)\,|\,\mathbf{a}\,|$. Thus the left- and right-hand expressions in (7) represent vectors with the same magnitude, direction and sense, so they are equal.

Case (2). Suppose that k, l are both negative, say $k = -p$,

$l = -q$, where p and q are both positive. Then by Case (1), $(p+q)\mathbf{a} = p\mathbf{a}+q\mathbf{a}$. Changing signs across, we find $(k+l)\mathbf{a} = k\mathbf{a}+l\mathbf{a}$.

Case (3). Suppose that k is positive, l negative, $|k| > |l|$. Let $p = k+l$, $q = -l$, so that p and q are positive and by Case (1) $(p+q)\mathbf{a} = p\mathbf{a}+q\mathbf{a}$, or $k\mathbf{a} = (k+l)\mathbf{a}-l\mathbf{a}$. Taking $l\mathbf{a}$ across to the left side of the equation we obtain Formula (7).

Case (4). k negative, l positive. $|k| > |l|$. The result follows from Case (3) by changing signs across.

Cases (5), (6). $k < 0$, $l > 0$, $|k| < |l|$; or: $k > 0$, $l < 0$, $|k| < |l|$. These follow from Cases 3, 4 by interchanging the numbers k, l and using the commutative law.

Case (7). If $k = 0$ or $l = 0$, or $k+l = 0$, or $\mathbf{a} = 0$, the result follows from Definition 4b and (2) or (3).

This completes the proof of (7).

Proof of (*8*). We only prove (8) in the case when k is a positive number, because the result is clear when $k = 0$, and the case $k < 0$ follows from $k > 0$ by changing signs across. Suppose that $k > 0$, then. Let OPQ be a triangle with vector sides $\overrightarrow{OP} = \mathbf{a}$, $\overrightarrow{PQ} = \mathbf{b}$, so that $\overrightarrow{OQ} = \mathbf{a}+\mathbf{b}$ (Fig. 12). Let O′P′Q′ be a triangle with sides parallel to the corresponding sides of OPQ and let

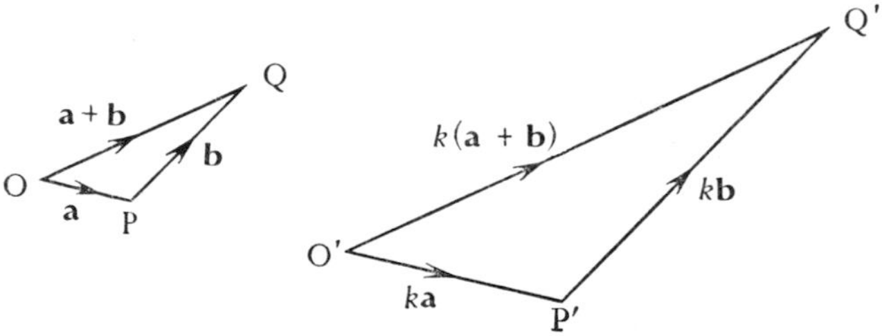

FIG. 12 Similar triangles and the distributive law.

$\overrightarrow{O'P'} = k\mathbf{a}$. Since the triangles OPQ, O′P′Q′ are similar, we have $\overrightarrow{P'Q'} = k\mathbf{b}$ and $\overrightarrow{O'Q'} = k\overrightarrow{OQ} = k(\mathbf{a}+\mathbf{b})$. Hence

$$k\mathbf{a}+k\mathbf{b} = \overrightarrow{O'P'}+\overrightarrow{P'Q'} = \overrightarrow{O'Q'} = k(\mathbf{a}+\mathbf{b}).$$

Strictly speaking, this proof does not cover the case when **a, b** have the same direction, and the reader should supply his own proof in this case.

Proof of (9). If any of the three symbols k, l or $\mathbf{a}$ represents a zero, formula (9) is true, since both sides of the equation represent the zero vector. We assume, therefore, that none of them is zero. The left- and right-hand sides then represent vectors with the same magnitude, namely $|k||l||\mathbf{a}|$, and the same direction, that of $|\mathbf{a}|$. The sense depends on the sign of the multiplier. Since two changes of sense return a vector to its original sense and two negatives multiply to give a positive, it is easy to verify that both sides of the equation agree in sense too.

11. Parallel vectors

Non-zero vectors which have the same direction are said to be *parallel*. It is clear from Definition 4 that if $\mathbf{a}$ is a non-zero vector and k is a non-zero number, then the vector $k\mathbf{a}$ is always parallel to the vector $\mathbf{a}$. Conversely, again from Definition 4, any vector $\mathbf{b}$ parallel to $\mathbf{a}$ can be expressed as a numerical multiple $k\mathbf{a}$. The multiplier k will be $\pm |\mathbf{b}|/|\mathbf{a}|$, the plus sign being taken if $\mathbf{a}, \mathbf{b}$ have the same sense and the minus sign if they have opposite senses. Thus we have the important result:

A vector $\mathbf{b}$ is parallel to a vector $\mathbf{a}$ if and only if there is a number $k \neq 0$ such that $\mathbf{b} = k\mathbf{a}$.

This means that if $\mathbf{b}$ and $\mathbf{a}$ are given, and k is regarded as unknown, the equation $\mathbf{b} = k\mathbf{a}$ does not always have a solution. There is no such thing as division of one vector by another. Number-vector multiplication is only the first of three kinds of multiplication to be defined in vector algebra, but they all have this in common—no division of vectors, in the sense of an operation inverse to multiplication, is possible.

Though division of one vector by another is not possible, it is permissible to cancel a *non-zero* vector from both sides of an equation, thus: if $k\mathbf{a} = l\mathbf{a}$, and $\mathbf{a} \neq \mathbf{0}$, then $k = l$. This kind of cancellation is occasionally useful.

Also, if k is a number different from zero, it is sometimes convenient to write $\dfrac{\mathbf{a}}{k}$ for the vector $\dfrac{1}{k}\mathbf{a}$. It follows from (9) that this vector is the unique solution $\mathbf{x}$ of the vector equation $k\mathbf{x} = \mathbf{a}$, so the process may be regarded as a form of division of a vector by a non-zero number.

12. Position vector

Let O be a point fixed in space, called the *origin*. Let P be any point. The vector $\overrightarrow{OP}$ is called the *position vector* of P, or, in the case of ambiguity about the origin, the position vector of P *relative to* O. If points P, Q have position vectors **p**, **q** respectively, then

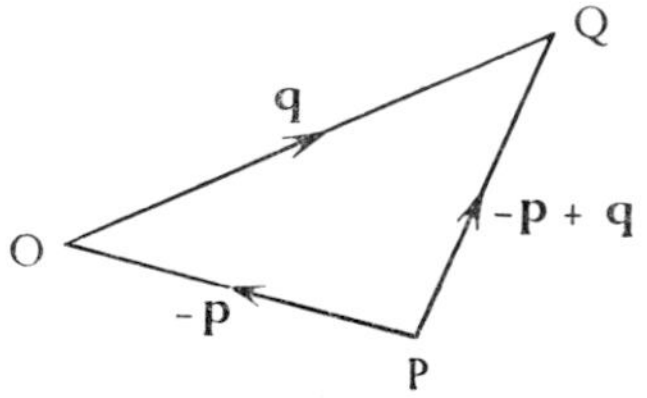

FIG. 13

$$\overrightarrow{PQ} = \mathbf{q}-\mathbf{p}. \tag{10}$$

For, from the triangle POQ, $\overrightarrow{PQ} = \overrightarrow{PO}+\overrightarrow{OQ} = -\mathbf{p}+\mathbf{q}$.

13. Point dividing a segment PQ in a given ratio

Suppose that two distinct points P, Q are given. Let X be a third point on the line PQ. The ratio of the lengths PX : XQ does not determine the point X, for there are two points with the same value of the ratio, one lying between P and Q, the other lying outside the segment PQ. In the first case the vectors $\overrightarrow{PX}$, $\overrightarrow{XQ}$ have the same sense, while in the second case their senses are opposite. It is convenient, therefore, to say that the ratio PX : XQ is positive if X lies between P and Q, but negative otherwise. With this convention, one value of the ratio will not give more than one point of the line. (There is no point X corresponding to the ratio PX : XQ $= -1$.)

Let X, P, Q be three collinear points, with position vectors **x**, **p**, **q** respectively. Suppose that PX : XQ $= k : l$, using the convention of sign just indicated. Then we shall show that

$$\mathbf{x} = \frac{k\mathbf{q}+l\mathbf{p}}{k+l}. \tag{11}$$

Proof. Using Definition 4, we have $\overrightarrow{PX} = \frac{k}{l}\overrightarrow{XQ}$, so, by (10), $l(\mathbf{x}-\mathbf{p}) = k(\mathbf{q}-\mathbf{x})$. Hence $(k+l)\mathbf{x} = k\mathbf{q}+l\mathbf{p}$, so

$$\mathbf{x} = \frac{k\mathbf{q}+l\mathbf{p}}{k+l},$$

as desired.

Corollary. If we take $k = l = 1$, we find that the position vector of the midpoint of PQ is $\frac{1}{2}(\mathbf{p}+\mathbf{q})$.

14. Centroid of a triangle

Let A, B, C be the vertices of a triangle, with position vectors **a, b, c** respectively. The midpoints L, M, N of the sides BC, CA, AB, in order, have position vectors, by (11)

$$\mathbf{l} = \tfrac{1}{2}(\mathbf{b}+\mathbf{c}), \quad \mathbf{m} = \tfrac{1}{2}(\mathbf{c}+\mathbf{a}), \quad \mathbf{n} = \tfrac{1}{2}(\mathbf{a}+\mathbf{b}).$$

Consider the point G on AL such that AG : GL = 2 : 1. By (11) its position vector is $\frac{1}{3}(\mathbf{a}+2\mathbf{l}) = \frac{1}{3}(\mathbf{a}+\mathbf{b}+\mathbf{c})$. This formula is unaltered if we change the order of the letters **a, b, c,** so G is also the point on BM such that BG : GM = 2 : 1 and the point on CN such that CG : GN = 2 : 1. We have thus proved, by vector methods, that the three medians of a triangle meet at a point, known as the centroid; that this point is a point of trisection of each median; and that its position vector is one-third of the vector sum of the position vectors of its vertices.

15. Worked examples

In working out examples, which will often be formulated in geometrical terms without any mention of vectors, the first step is to choose an origin and name the position vectors of the various points. It is usually best to take corresponding letters for a point and its position vector, so that the point A, for example, will have position vector **a**, and the vector $\overrightarrow{AB}$ will be $\mathbf{b}-\mathbf{a}$. There must be some exceptions to this convenient rule, though, since the origin, even if it is not labelled O, must always have position vector **0**.

Our first example concerns the *tetrahedron*, the solid figure which is the natural generalization of a triangle. It consists of four non-coplanar points, A, B, C, D, the four triangles ABC, ABD, ACD, BCD called its *faces*, and the six line-segments AB, AC, AD, BC, BD, CD called its *edges*. Two edges which do not meet at a vertex are called *opposite* edges. There are three pairs of opposite edges: AB, CD; AC, BD; AD, BC.

Example 1. Show that the three line-segments joining the midpoints of pairs of opposite edges of a tetrahedron bisect each other.

Solution. Let A, B, C, D have position vectors, in order, **a, b,**

c, **d**. (This convention—same letter for point and position vector—will be used from now on without repeated mention.) If L, M are the midpoints of AB, CD, then

$$\mathbf{l} = \tfrac{1}{2}(\mathbf{a}+\mathbf{b}), \quad \mathbf{m} = \tfrac{1}{2}(\mathbf{c}+\mathbf{d}),$$

and the midpoint P of LM has position vector

$$\mathbf{p} = \tfrac{1}{2}(\mathbf{l}+\mathbf{m}) = \tfrac{1}{4}(\mathbf{a}+\mathbf{b}+\mathbf{c}+\mathbf{d}).$$

Now this expression is symmetrical, unaltered by changing the order of the points A, B, C, D. Therefore P is also the midpoint of the segment joining the midpoint of AC to that of BD and also

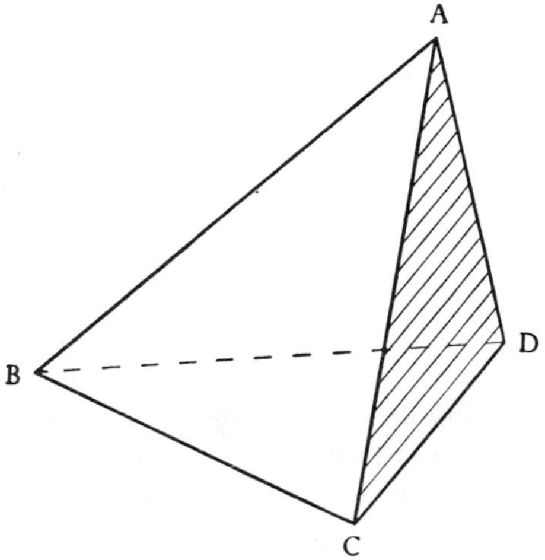

FIG. 14

the midpoint of the segment joining the midpoint of AD to that of BC, and all three segments bisect each other as required.

The point P obtained above is called the *centroid* of the tetrahedron.

Example 2. ABCD is a parallelogram and E is the midpoint of AB. Prove by vector methods that DE and AC trisect one another.

Solution. Choose A as origin, so that $\mathbf{b} = \overrightarrow{AB}$ is the position vector of B and $\mathbf{d} = \overrightarrow{AD}$ is the position vector of D. Since ABCD is a parallelogram, $\mathbf{c} = \overrightarrow{AC} = \mathbf{b}+\mathbf{d}$. By (11) the position vector of E is $\frac{1}{2}\mathbf{b}$. There are two points of trisection of DE and two of AC. Working out their position vectors from (11), we find

trisecting AC: $\frac{1}{3}(\mathbf{b}+\mathbf{d})$, $\frac{2}{3}(\mathbf{b}+\mathbf{d})$,

trisecting DE: $\frac{2}{3}\mathbf{d}+\frac{1}{6}\mathbf{b}$, $\frac{1}{3}\mathbf{b}+\frac{1}{3}\mathbf{d}$.

Example 2 illustrates a method of showing that two given lines cut in a certain ratio, by using formula (11) to show that the points of subdivision coincide. To apply it in the form above it is necessary to know, or to guess in advance, what the ratio of subdivision is going to be. The calculation of the position vector of the centroid in § 14 is similar in this respect. However, the next example shows that this type of method can be modified, by using unknown ratios which are later adjusted, so as to apply to problems where the ratio is not known in advance.

Example 3. Coplanar points A, B, A′, B′ have position vectors $\mathbf{a}$, $\mathbf{b}$, $r\mathbf{a}$, $s\mathbf{b}$, in that order, where $\mathbf{a}$, $\mathbf{b}$ are non-zero and not parallel. Find the position vector of the point of intersection of the lines AB, A′B′.

Solution. Let X be the desired point. Since X lies on the line AB, the vectors $\overrightarrow{AX}$, $\overrightarrow{AB}$ are parallel, that is, there is a number k such that $\overrightarrow{AX} = k\overrightarrow{AB}$, or,

$$\mathbf{x}-\mathbf{a} = k(\mathbf{b}-\mathbf{a}). \qquad \text{(i)}$$

Similarly X lies on the line A′B′, so there is a number l such that $\overrightarrow{A'X} = l\,\overrightarrow{A'B'}$, or,

$$\mathbf{x}-r\mathbf{a} = l(s\mathbf{b}-r\mathbf{a}). \qquad \text{(ii)}$$

Subtracting equation (ii) from equation (i) and simplifying, we find

$$-(\,(1-k)-r(1-l)\,)\mathbf{a} = (k-sl)\mathbf{b}. \qquad \text{(iii)}$$

If both sides of (iii) were non-zero, we should have a vector parallel to $\mathbf{a}$ on the left equal to a vector parallel to $\mathbf{b}$ on the right, and that is impossible since $\mathbf{a}$ is not parallel to $\mathbf{b}$. Thus both sides of (iii) are zero vectors, and since neither $\mathbf{a}$ nor $\mathbf{b}$ is zero, the coefficients are zero, that is,

$$\{(1-k)-r(1-l)\} = k-sl = 0.$$

Added together, these equations give $(1-r) = (s-r)\,l$. On substituting the value $(1-r)/(s-r)$ for l in (2), we get the answer

$$x = \frac{(s-1)r\mathbf{a}+(1-r)s\mathbf{b}}{s-r}.$$

This formula is meaningless when $s = r$, since division by zero is impossible; but no answer can be expected in that case, because then the lines are parallel.

Exercises on Chapter 2

1. The position vectors of points A, B, C, D are respectively $\mathbf{a}$, $\mathbf{b}$, $3\mathbf{a}+\mathbf{b}$, $-\mathbf{a}+2\mathbf{b}$. Express in terms of $\mathbf{a}$, $\mathbf{b}$ the vectors $\overrightarrow{AB}$, $\overrightarrow{AC}$, $\overrightarrow{AD}$, $\overrightarrow{BC}$, $\overrightarrow{BD}$, $\overrightarrow{CD}$. Find also the position vectors of the midpoints of the segments AB, BC, CD, DA and the centroids of the triangles ABC, ACD, BCD.

2. ABCD is a parallelogram and $\mathbf{a}$, $\mathbf{b}$, $\mathbf{c}$ are the position vectors of A, B, C. What is the position vector of D?

3. Give an alternative proof that the position vector of the midpoint of PQ is $\frac{1}{2}(\mathbf{p}+\mathbf{q})$ by constructing the parallelogram POQR, O being the origin.

4. If L, M, N are the midpoints of BC, CA, AB respectively and O is any point, show that

(i) $\overrightarrow{OA}+\overrightarrow{OB}+\overrightarrow{OC} = \overrightarrow{OL}+\overrightarrow{OM}+\overrightarrow{ON}$,

(ii) $\overrightarrow{AL}+\overrightarrow{BM}+\overrightarrow{CN} = \mathbf{0}$.

5. ABC, A′B′C′ are two triangles and G, G′ their centroids. Prove that $\overrightarrow{AA'}+\overrightarrow{BB'}+\overrightarrow{CC'} = 3\,\overrightarrow{GG'}$.

6. Six points A, B, C, D, E, F are given in space. P, Q, R, S are centroids of the triangles ABC, ABD, DEF, CEF. Show that P, Q, R, S are the vertices of a parallelogram.

7. A, B, C, D are four points not all in the same plane. P, Q, R, S, T, U are the midpoints of AB, BC, CD, DA, AC, BD respectively. Prove that PQRS, PTRU, QTSU are all parallelograms.

8. If $\mathbf{a}$, $\mathbf{b}$, $\mathbf{c}$, $\mathbf{d}$ are position vectors of the vertices A, B, C, D of a tetrahedron, show that the lines joining the vertices to the centroids of the faces opposite them meet at the point G with position vector

$\frac{1}{4}(\mathbf{a}+\mathbf{b}+\mathbf{c}+\mathbf{d})$. A′, B′, C′ are points on AD, BD, CD such that

$$AA'/A'D = BB'/B'D = CC'/C'D = \tfrac{1}{3}.$$

Show that G is the centroid of A′B′C′.

9. If ABCD and A′B′C′D′ are two parallelograms not necessarily in the same plane, show that the midpoints of AA′, BB′, CC′, DD′ are also vertices of a parallelogram.

10. If O, G, H are the circumcentre, centroid and orthocentre of a triangle ABC, show that O, G, H are collinear and that G trisects OH. (Use the formulae of § 8, § 14.)

11. Suppose that ABCDEF is a regular hexagon inscribed in a circle centre O, radius r. Let $\overrightarrow{AB} = \mathbf{p}$, $\overrightarrow{BC} = \mathbf{q}$. Express in terms of **p**, **q** the vectors $\overrightarrow{CD}$, $\overrightarrow{DE}$, $\overrightarrow{EF}$, $\overrightarrow{FA}$ and also the vectors $\overrightarrow{OA}$, $\overrightarrow{OB}$, etc. Show that the orthocentres of the triangles ABC, BCD, ... , FAB, also form a regular hexagon and lie on a circle centre O and radius $2r$.

12. Four non-coplanar points A, B, C, D lie at equal distances from a point O. A point P is defined by the vector equation

$$2\,\overrightarrow{OP} = \overrightarrow{OA}+\overrightarrow{OB}+\overrightarrow{OC}+\overrightarrow{OD}.$$

Show that the line joining P to the midpoint of any edge of the tetrahedron ABCD is at right angles to the opposite edge.

13. Suppose that O is the centre of a circle $A_1A_2A_3$ of unit radius in a plane Π. If the point B_1 is the point defined by the vector relation $\overrightarrow{OB_1} = \overrightarrow{OA_2}+\overrightarrow{OA_3}$, show that B_1 is the centre of the other circle of unit radius in Π which passes through A_2 and A_3. If, further, two other circles of unit radius and centres B_2 and B_3 are drawn through A_3, A_1 and A_1, A_2 respectively, prove that the three circles centres B_1, B_2, B_3 meet at C where $\overrightarrow{OC} = \overrightarrow{OA_1}+\overrightarrow{OA_2}+\overrightarrow{OA_3}$.

3

PROJECTIONS, COMPONENTS, COORDINATES

1. Introduction

The advantages of using coordinates (distances from two perpendicular axes) to label the points of a plane are well known. Coordinates are just as useful in solid geometry, but now three mutually perpendicular axes are needed instead of two, and every point has three coordinates. We shall see in this chapter that the vectors, as well as the points, of space can be labelled by means of numbers called *components*. The two ideas are related, for the coordinates of a point are the components of its position vector.

We shall find out in this chapter how to write down the components of the sum of two vectors or of a numerical multiple of a vector, and, in later chapters, when we define different kinds of vector multiplication, we shall see how they can be expressed in terms of components too. It will then be possible to translate every vector equation into either one number equation or three number equations—three, because each vector has three components. Though the component form of equation is more cumbersome, it is often needed in practical calculations, so one must be thoroughly familiar with it. Historically, the component form is the original form in which many of these equations first occurred, and in a sense vector algebra developed as a shorthand method of writing numerical equations. When the component form of some of these relations is compared with the short and simple vector form, it will be clear why vector notation has superseded the other whenever possible.

2. Unit vector

A vector $\mathbf{u}$ is called a *unit vector* if its length $|\mathbf{u}|$ is equal to 1. If $\mathbf{a}$ is any non-zero vector, there are two unit vectors parallel to $\mathbf{a}$: $\mathbf{a}/|\mathbf{a}|$ with the same sense, and $-\mathbf{a}/|\mathbf{a}|$ with the opposite sense. If $\mathbf{u}$ is a unit vector with a given direction, then any vector (unit or not) with that direction has the form $k\mathbf{u}$, the number k being equal, apart from sign, to the length of the vector.

3. Orthogonal decomposition of a vector. Projections.

Let $\mathbf{u} = \overrightarrow{OL}$ be a unit vector, Π the plane through O perpendicular to $\mathbf{u}$ and let $\mathbf{a} = \overrightarrow{OA}$ be an arbitrary vector (Fig. 15). If P is the foot of the perpendicular from A on Π, then $\mathbf{a} = \overrightarrow{OP}+\overrightarrow{PA}$, so any vector $\mathbf{a}$ can be expressed as the sum of two vectors, one ($\overrightarrow{PA}$) parallel to $\mathbf{u}$ and the other ($\overrightarrow{OP}$) perpendicular to $\mathbf{u}$. Since any vector parallel to $\mathbf{u}$ is a numerical multiple of $\mathbf{u}$, we have

$$\mathbf{a} = a_1\mathbf{u}+\mathbf{p} \qquad (\mathbf{p}, \mathbf{u} \text{ at right angles}). \tag{1}$$

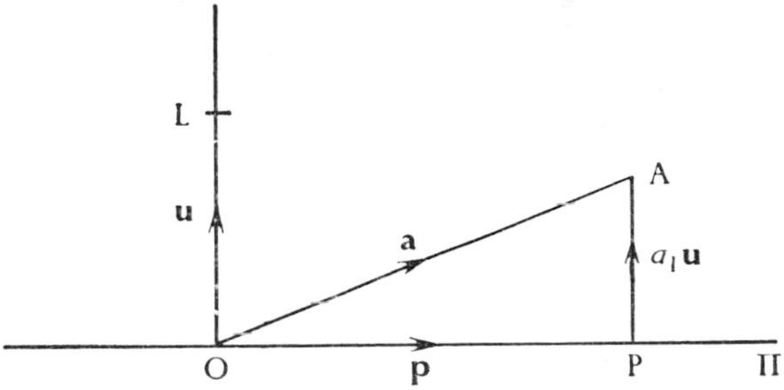

FIG. 15

When $\mathbf{u}$ has been fixed, there is only one such expression for $\mathbf{a}$, since, if there were two, say

$$\mathbf{a} = a_1\mathbf{u}+\mathbf{p} = b_1\mathbf{u}+\mathbf{q} \quad (\mathbf{q}, \mathbf{p} \text{ both at right angles to } \mathbf{u}),$$

we should have, on subtracting,

$$(a_1-b_1)\mathbf{u} = \mathbf{q}-\mathbf{p}.$$

If the left and right expressions of this equation were not both zero vectors, then one would be parallel to $\mathbf{u}$ and the other would be perpendicular to $\mathbf{u}$ and they could not be equal. Thus both sides are zero, from which we deduce that $a_1 = b_1$ and $\mathbf{p} = \mathbf{q}$. In other words the two expressions for $\mathbf{a}$ are the same, and the resolution of $\mathbf{a}$ into a vector parallel to $\mathbf{u}$ and a vector perpendicular to $\mathbf{u}$ is indeed unique.

The number a_1 defined by equation (1) is called the *projection* of $\mathbf{a}$ on the unit vector $\mathbf{u}$. If $\mathbf{v}$ is a non-zero vector, not necessarily a unit vector, the projection of $\mathbf{a}$ on $\mathbf{v}$ is defined to be the same as the projection of **a** on the unit vector $\mathbf{u} = \mathbf{v}/|\mathbf{v}|$ with the same direction and sense as **v**. If θ is the angle between **a** and **v**, that is, if θ is the amount of rotation needed to bring the direction and sense of **a** into line with those of **v**, then it is seen from the right-angled triangle OPA (Fig. 15) that the projection of **a** on **v** is $|\mathbf{a}| \cos\theta$. The angle θ may be assumed positive, since a sense of rotation in the plane OAP has not been defined, and in any case $\cos\theta = \cos(-\theta)$.

The vector **p** defined by equation (1) is called the *projection of* **a** *on the plane* Π. Notice that the projection of a vector on a plane is a vector, whereas the projection of a vector on another vector is a number.

4. Projections of sums and multiples of vectors

Let **u** be a unit vector and Π a plane at right angles to **u**. If **x** is any vector, let $p(\mathbf{x})$ denote the projection of **x** on **u** and let $\mathbf{P}(\mathbf{x})$ denote the projection of **x** on Π. Bold type is used for the projection on the plane Π, because it is a vector, and italic type for the other projection, which is a number. The relations defining the projections of two vectors **a**, **b** are then

$$\mathbf{a} = p(\mathbf{a})\mathbf{u}+\mathbf{P}(\mathbf{a}) \qquad (\mathbf{P}(\mathbf{a}) \text{ at right angles to } \mathbf{u}),$$
$$\mathbf{b} = p(\mathbf{b})\mathbf{u}+\mathbf{P}(\mathbf{b}) \qquad (\mathbf{P}(\mathbf{b}) \text{ at right angles to } \mathbf{u}).$$

Added together, these give

$$\mathbf{a}+\mathbf{b} = [p(\mathbf{a})+p(\mathbf{b})]\mathbf{u}+[\mathbf{P}(\mathbf{a})+\mathbf{P}(\mathbf{b})]. \qquad (2)$$

$\mathbf{P}(\mathbf{a})+\mathbf{P}(\mathbf{b})$, the sum of two vectors parallel to Π, is itself parallel to Π. Thus equation (2) expresses $\mathbf{a}+\mathbf{b}$ as a sum of two vectors, one parallel to **u** and one perpendicular to **u**. The first member of the sum, by definition, is the projection of $\mathbf{a}+\mathbf{b}$ on **u**, and the second member is its projection on Π. In symbols:

$$p(\mathbf{a}+\mathbf{b}) = p(\mathbf{a})+p(\mathbf{b}), \qquad \mathbf{P}(\mathbf{a}+\mathbf{b}) = \mathbf{P}(\mathbf{a})+\mathbf{P}(\mathbf{b}). \qquad (3)$$

In a similar way, multiplying the first equation by a number k, we find

$$p(k\mathbf{a}) = kp(\mathbf{a}), \qquad \mathbf{P}(k\mathbf{a}) = k\mathbf{P}(\mathbf{a}). \qquad (4)$$

5. Components of a vector

Carrying the process of § 3 a step further, take three unit vectors, $\mathbf{u}_1 = \overrightarrow{OL}$, $\mathbf{u}_2 = \overrightarrow{OM}$, $\mathbf{u}_3 = \overrightarrow{ON}$, each perpendicular to the other two. Let $\mathbf{a} = \overrightarrow{OA}$ be an arbitrary vector. As before, drop AP perpendicular to the plane MON. Within the plane MON drop PQ perpendicular to the line ON.

Then $$\mathbf{a} = \overrightarrow{OQ}+\overrightarrow{QP}+\overrightarrow{PA}. \tag{5}$$

The vectors $\overrightarrow{PA}$, $\overrightarrow{QP}$, $\overrightarrow{OQ}$, parallel, in order to $\mathbf{u}_1$, $\mathbf{u}_2$, $\mathbf{u}_3$, are multiples $a_1\mathbf{u}_1$, $a_2\mathbf{u}_2$, $a_3\mathbf{u}_3$, and (5) becomes

$$\mathbf{a} = a_1\mathbf{u}_1+a_2\mathbf{u}_2+a_3\mathbf{u}_3. \tag{6}$$

The expression of $\mathbf{a}$ in the form (6) is unique, for in any such

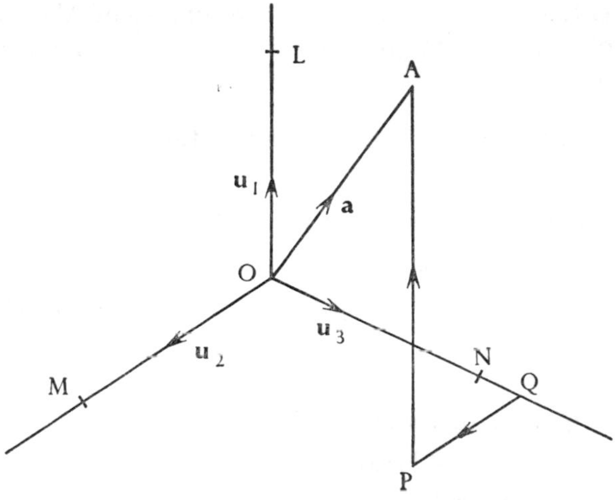

FIG. 16

expression a_1 must be the projection of $\mathbf{a}$ on $\mathbf{u}_1$, since $a_2\mathbf{u}_2+a_3\mathbf{u}_3$ is at right angles to $\mathbf{u}$. Similarly a_2 is the projection of $\mathbf{a}$ on $\mathbf{u}_2$ and a_3 its projection on $\mathbf{u}_3$. The quantities a_1, a_2, a_3 are called the *components of* $\mathbf{a}$ *relative to the base* $\mathbf{u}_1$, $\mathbf{u}_2$, $\mathbf{u}_3$. When there is no ambiguity about the base, the vector with components a_1, a_2, a_3 will be denoted by (a_1, a_2, a_3).

6. Coordinates of a point

Suppose that we are given a fixed point O called the *origin* and a base consisting of three mutually perpendicular unit vectors $\mathbf{u}_1$, $\mathbf{u}_2$, $\mathbf{u}_3$. Such a collection (O, $\mathbf{u}_1$, $\mathbf{u}_2$, $\mathbf{u}_3$) is said to form a *coordinate system*. If A is any point and $\mathbf{a} = \overrightarrow{OA}$ its position vector relative to O, the components (a_1, a_2, a_3) of $\mathbf{a}$ are called the *coordinates* of A (relative to the given coordinate system).

We shall not always distinguish between points and their position vectors. Thus 'the point $\mathbf{a}$' will mean the point with position vector $\mathbf{a}$, and the expression (a_1, a_2, a_3) may mean, according to context, either the point with these coordinates or the vector with these components.

There are infinitely many possible coordinate systems, and the same point P will have different coordinates in different systems. A careful choice of coordinate system can often simplify calculations. Usually only one coordinate system will be used throughout an argument, and one refers to the 'coordinates of A' or 'the components of $\mathbf{a}$', without repeatedly specifying the origin and base-vectors.

7. Formulae for vector operations in terms of components

(*i*) *Addition*

Let $\mathbf{a}$ and $\mathbf{b}$ be two vectors, with known components

$$\mathbf{a} = (a_1, a_2, a_3) \quad \text{and} \quad \mathbf{b} = (b_1, b_2, b_3).$$

We wish to find the components of their sum $\mathbf{a}+\mathbf{b}$. From equation (6),

$$\mathbf{a} = a_1\mathbf{u}_1+a_2\mathbf{u}_2+a_3\mathbf{u}_3, \qquad \mathbf{b} = b_1\mathbf{u}_1+b_2\mathbf{u}_2+b_3\mathbf{u}_3.$$

Hence, by the laws of vector algebra,

$$\mathbf{a}+\mathbf{b} = (a_1+b_1)\mathbf{u}_1+(a_2+b_2)\mathbf{u}_2+(a_3+b_3)\mathbf{u}_3.$$

Thus the vector $\mathbf{a}+\mathbf{b}$ has components $(a_1+b_1, a_2+b_2, a_3+b_3)$.

Each component of the sum is obtained by adding together the corresponding components of the two vectors.

(*ii*) *Number–vector multiplication*

Let $\mathbf{a} = (a_1, a_2, a_3)$ and let k be a number. We wish to find the components of the vector $k\mathbf{a}$. We have

$$k\mathbf{a} = k(a_1\mathbf{u}_1+a_2\mathbf{u}_2+a_3\mathbf{u}_3) = ka_1\mathbf{u}_1+ka_2\mathbf{u}_2+ka_3\mathbf{u}_3$$
$$= (ka_1, ka_2, ka_3).$$

Each component of $k\mathbf{a}$ is obtained by multiplying the corresponding component of $\mathbf{a}$ by k.

Note. Since a_1, a_2, a_3 are projections of $\mathbf{a}$ on the corresponding unit vectors, the two formulae just obtained could be regarded as special cases of those of § 4.

(*iii*) *Length of a vector.* In equation (5) of this chapter, the vectors $\overrightarrow{OQ}$, $\overrightarrow{QP}$, $\overrightarrow{PA}$ are mutually perpendicular. By Pythagoras's Theorem,

$$|\overrightarrow{OA}|^2 = |\overrightarrow{OQ}|^2 + |\overrightarrow{QP}|^2 + |\overrightarrow{PA}|^2.$$

Hence
$$|\mathbf{a}|^2 = a_1{}^2 + a_2{}^2 + a_3{}^2.$$

The square of the length of a vector is the sum of the squares of its components.

8. Application of the formulae

Some numerical examples are now given, illustrating the use of the formulae of § 7.

Example 1. If

$$\mathbf{a} = (-1, 3, 4),\ \mathbf{b} = (2, -2, -1) \text{ and } \mathbf{c} = (3, -1, 0),$$

find

(i) the components of the vector $3\mathbf{a}-4\mathbf{b}+7\mathbf{c}$,
(ii) the length of the vector $\mathbf{a}+\mathbf{b}$.

(i) Where two or more vectors are to be added, it is convenient to write the vectors underneath one another, the numbers in each column being then added. Using 7 (ii) we have

$$\begin{aligned} 3\mathbf{a} &= (-3, 9, 12) \\ -4\mathbf{b} &= (-8, 8, 4) \\ 7\mathbf{c} &= (21, -7, 0). \end{aligned}$$

Adding the numbers in the separate columns we obtain the sum

$$3\mathbf{a}-4\mathbf{b}+7\mathbf{c} = (10, 10, 16).$$

(ii) As under (i) we find $\mathbf{a}+\mathbf{b} = (1, 1, 3)$. By 7 (iii) we have $|\mathbf{a}+\mathbf{b}| = \sqrt{(1^2+1^2+3^2)} = \sqrt{11}$.

Example 2. Find the lengths of the sides of the triangle whose vertices are the points A$(-1, -1, -1)$, B$(2, -1, 2)$, C$(2, 1, 0)$. A point P divides AB internally in the ratio AP : PB = 2 : 1. Find the coordinates of P and show that BPC is a right angle.

Use $\mathbf{p}, \mathbf{a}, \mathbf{b}, \mathbf{c}$ for the position vectors of P, A, B, C. By Chapter 2, § 13,

$$\mathbf{p} = \frac{\mathbf{a}+2\mathbf{b}}{1+2} = (1, -1, 1);$$

the coordinates being worked out as in Example 1. From Chapter 2, § 11, $\overrightarrow{BC} = \mathbf{c}-\mathbf{b} = (0, 2, -2)$, so by 7 (iii) the length of the side BC is $\sqrt{8}$. Similarly the lengths of the sides CA, AB can be worked out and are found to be $\sqrt{14}$, $\sqrt{18}$. We also find

$$\overrightarrow{PB} = (1,0,1), \overrightarrow{PC} = (1,2,-1), \text{so } PB^2+PC^2 = 2+6 = 8 = BC^2.$$

Thus BPC is a right angle by the converse of Pythagoras's Theorem. (A better method of testing whether two vectors are perpendicular will be given in the next chapter.)

Example 3. Under what conditions is the vector (a_1, a_2, a_3) parallel to the vector (b_1, b_2, b_3)?

If the vectors **a**, **b** are parallel, then $\mathbf{b} = k\mathbf{a}$, where k is a number. Comparing components, $b_1 = ka_1$, $b_2 = ka_2$, $b_3 = ka_3$. Assuming that a_1, a_2, a_3 are all different from zero, we may eliminate k to obtain

$$\frac{b_1}{a_1} = \frac{b_2}{a_2} = \frac{b_3}{a_3}, \quad \text{or} \quad a_1 : a_2 : a_3 = b_1 : b_2 : b_3.$$

(Though division by zero is impossible, this condition can be used (cautiously) when zeros occur if we make the convention that 0/0 can take any value; so that, if any component of **a** vanishes, the same component of **b** must also vanish. When in doubt, one should always use the basic condition $\mathbf{b} = k\mathbf{a}$.)

Example 4. Are the following points collinear?

$$A(1, 2, 3), \quad B(3, 3, 2), \quad C(7, 5, 0).$$

The points A, B, C are collinear if the vectors $\overrightarrow{AB}$, $\overrightarrow{AC}$ have the same direction. By subtraction

$$\overrightarrow{AB} = (2, 1, -1) \quad \text{and} \quad \overrightarrow{AC} = (6, 3, -3).$$

The condition for parallelism (Example 3) is satisfied:

$$\frac{6}{2} = \frac{3}{1} = \frac{-3}{-1}.$$

Thus the points are collinear.

9. Components and coordinates in plane geometry

Suppose that we are considering only vectors in a fixed plane. Let $\mathbf{u}_1$ be a unit vector in the plane and let $\mathbf{u}_2$ be the vector obtained by rotating $\mathbf{u}_1$ through a right angle anticlockwise. An arbitrary vector **a** in the plane will clearly be expressible in the form $a_1\mathbf{u}_1+a_2\mathbf{u}_2$, and may be thought of as having only two components (a_1, a_2). Just as in space, the components of a sum of two vectors will be the sum of the corresponding components of the individual vectors.

There is another way of labelling the vectors of the plane. A vector **a** is completely specified if we know its magnitude r and the

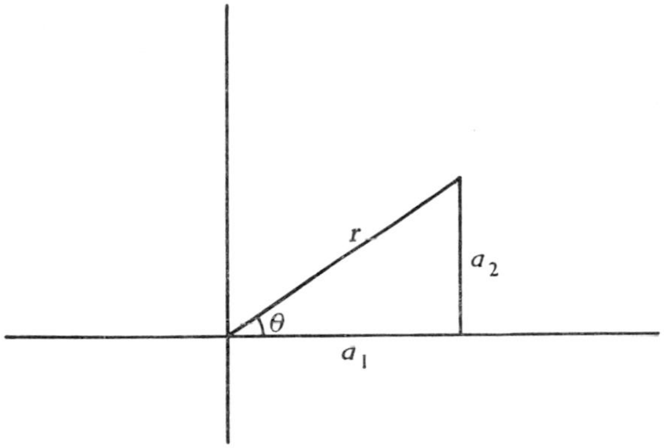

FIG. 17

angle θ, measured anticlockwise, needed to rotate the unit vector $\mathbf{u}_1$ to such a position that its direction and sense are the same as those of **a**. The quantities r, θ are called the *polar coordinates* of the plane vector **a**, and we write $\mathbf{a} = [r, \theta]$. Clearly (Fig. 17), the polar coordinates are related to the components by the equations

$$a_1 = r\cos\theta, \qquad a_2 = r\sin\theta. \tag{7}$$

We shall now use these ideas to give a vector proof of the formulae in trigonometry for the sum of two sines and the sum of two cosines. Suppose we have two plane vectors of equal magnitude r, say $\mathbf{a} = \overrightarrow{\mathrm{OA}} = [r, \theta]$, and $\mathbf{b} = \overrightarrow{\mathrm{OB}} = [r, \phi]$.

The triangle OAB is isosceles, and the symmetry of the figure shows that if P is the midpoint of AB then OP is at right angles to AB and bisects the angle between OA and OB. Thus the angle between $\overrightarrow{OP}$ and $\mathbf{u}_1$ is $\frac{1}{2}(\theta+\phi)$ and the magnitude of $\overrightarrow{OP}$, from the right-angled triangle OPA, is $r\cos\frac{1}{2}(\theta-\phi)$. Comparing components in the formula $\overrightarrow{OP} = \frac{1}{2}(\overrightarrow{OA}+\overrightarrow{OB})$, we deduce, after simplification

$$\cos\theta+\cos\phi = 2\cos\tfrac{1}{2}(\theta-\phi)\cos\tfrac{1}{2}(\theta+\phi),$$
$$\sin\theta+\sin\phi = 2\cos\tfrac{1}{2}(\theta-\phi)\sin\tfrac{1}{2}(\theta+\phi).$$

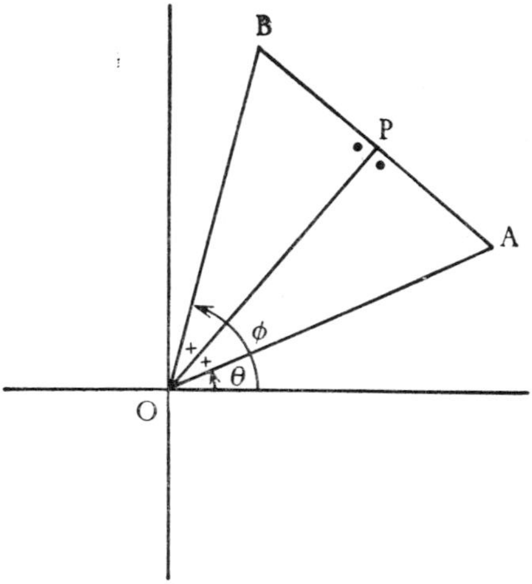

FIG. 18

10. The use of vectors in plane geometry

In plane geometry too, as in space, the coordinates of a point are the components of its position vector, and this is sometimes a helpful way of looking at problems, although it does not simplify as dramatically as in solid geometry. As an example, we shall study in the next section the problem of finding the equations of transformation from one coordinate system in the plane to another. The method given is not different in principle from the standard method contained in textbooks of coordinate geometry, but it is better because the argument clearly works for rotation through any angle from 0 to 2π, and for points whose coordinates have any sign. Textbooks on coordinate geometry do not as a rule pay much attention to these points, and a study of the diagrams in the section on rotation of axes will reveal that they really deal only with the case of rotation through an acute angle and points whose coordinates are positive in both systems—rather severe limitations! A large number of separate diagrams and detailed consideration of signs would be needed to make sure of the formula in its complete generality. When one uses vector algebra, however, all possibilities of different sign are included, since the distributive laws apply with multipliers of all signs. The trouble of considering seven separate cases in the discussion of these laws is well worth while, because on so many later occasions, like this one, a discussion of separate cases is avoided.

11. Change of coordinate system in the plane

Let XOY be a cartesian coordinate system in the plane. If **u** is the unit vector with the direction and sense of OX and **v** is the unit vector with the direction and sense of OY, then it is clear that the coordinates (x, y) of a point P are given by the vector equation

$$\overrightarrow{\mathrm{OP}} = x\mathbf{u}+y\mathbf{v}. \tag{8}$$

The reader should check, by drawing pictures to represent points P in all four quadrants, that the above equation always gives the correct sign for the coordinates. We shall always assume that our coordinate systems are right-handed, so that **v** is obtained by rotation of **u** anticlockwise through an angle $\frac{1}{2}\pi$.

Suppose now that X′O′Y′ is another cartesian coordinate system, **u′** the unit vector with direction and sense of O′X′ and **v′** the unit vector with the direction and sense of O′Y′. The same point P will have coordinates (x', y') (usually, of course, different from x, y) in the new system, where

$$\overrightarrow{\mathrm{O'P}} = x'\mathbf{u}'+y'\mathbf{v}'. \tag{9}$$

It is obviously useful to be able to change our coordinate system to simplify calculations in particular problems, but if we do vary the coordinate system we must know what is happening to the coordinates of each point when the change is made.

We consider the operation of changing from the XOY-system to the X′O′Y′-system, so we shall call the XOY-system the *old* system and (x, y) the old coordinates of the point P. Similarly, X′O′Y′ is called the *new* system, and (x', y') the new coordinates of the point P. We wish to find equations which will give us x, y when we know x', y', and conversely.

Throughout the argument, we shall reserve the component notation (l, m) for the vector whose components are l, m in the *old* system: $(l, m) = l\mathbf{u}+m\mathbf{v}$. To avoid confusion, the vector whose components are l, m in the new system will have to be written out in full, $l\mathbf{u}'+m\mathbf{v}'$.

Before we can obtain equations, we require some information about the relative position of the two coordinate systems—the *old* coordinates of the *new* origin O′, which we suppose are (h, k), and the angle θ of rotation anticlockwise required to bring the old axes into a position parallel to the new ones. Then the polar coordinates of $\mathbf{u}'$ in the old system are $[1, \theta]$, so, by (7)

$$\mathbf{u}' = (\cos\theta, \sin\theta).$$

Since $\mathbf{v}'$ is obtained by a further rotation $\frac{1}{2}\pi$ from $\mathbf{u}'$, we have

$$\mathbf{v}' = (\cos(\theta+\tfrac{1}{2}\pi), \sin(\theta+\tfrac{1}{2}\pi)) = (-\sin\theta, \cos\theta).$$

Also, $\overrightarrow{\mathrm{OO'}} = (h, k)$, and $\overrightarrow{\mathrm{OP}} = (x, y)$. Hence, using equation (9),

$$\begin{aligned}(x, y) &= \overrightarrow{\mathrm{OP}} = \overrightarrow{\mathrm{OO'}}+\overrightarrow{\mathrm{O'P}} = \overrightarrow{\mathrm{OO'}}+x'\mathbf{u}'+y'\mathbf{v}'\\ &= (h, k)+x'(\cos\theta, \sin\theta)+y'(-\sin\theta, \cos\theta).\end{aligned}$$

Comparing components,

$$\begin{aligned}x &= h+x'\cos\theta-y'\sin\theta,\\ y &= k+x'\sin\theta+y'\cos\theta.\end{aligned}$$

Two special cases of this formula are particularly important. If we put $\theta = 0$, we obtain the formula for *change of origin, with parallel axes*:

$$x = x'+h, \qquad y = y'+k. \tag{10}$$

The formula giving the new coordinates in terms of the old is, in this case:

$$x' = x-h, \qquad y' = y-k. \tag{11}$$

If, on the other hand, we put $h = k = 0$ in the general formula, we obtain the formula for *rotation of axes, with origin fixed*:

$$x = x'\cos\theta-y'\sin\theta, \qquad y = x'\sin\theta+y'\cos\theta. \tag{12}$$

Either by solving these equations for x', y', or, by noticing that the old axes arise from the new by a rotation $-\theta$, we obtain the reverse equations:

$$x' = x\cos\theta+y\sin\theta, \qquad y' = -x\sin\theta+y\cos\theta. \tag{13}$$

Any change of coordinates in the plane can be done in two steps, a change of origin only, followed by a rotation of axes only, so the formulae (10) to (13) are all that are needed. The general formula at the beginning is hardly ever used.

12. Worked example

The reader will find plenty of applications of the formulae of the last section in any textbook of plane coordinate geometry. Sometimes equations can be simplified by changing the coordinate system so that certain coefficients vanish in the new equation. It seems worth while to work one example.

Example. Position in the plane is defined by two systems of coordinates, (x, y) and (x', y'). The origins are the same, but the (x', y')-axes are obtained by rotation θ anticlockwise from the (x, y)-axes. In the (x, y)-system a certain locus has equation

$$x^2+3xy+(1+\surd 3)y^2 = 1.$$

Obtain a value of θ which will ensure that the (x', y')-equation of this locus has no term in $x'y'$.

Solution. The new equation is obtained from the old by substituting for x, y in terms of x', y' from equations (12). We find

$$\begin{aligned}&(x'\cos\theta-y'\sin\theta)^2+\\&+3(x'\cos\theta-y'\sin\theta)(x'\sin\theta+y'\cos\theta)+\\&+(1+\surd 3)(x'\sin\theta+y'\cos\theta)^2\\&=1\end{aligned}$$

The coefficient of $x'y'$ is

$$-2\cos\theta\sin\theta+3(\cos^2\theta-\sin^2\theta)+2(1+\surd 3)\cos\theta\sin\theta$$
$$= 3\cos 2\theta+\surd 3\sin 2\theta.$$

If this is zero, $\tan 2\theta = -\surd 3$. A solution is $2\theta = \frac{2}{3}\pi$, $\theta = \frac{1}{3}\pi$. Then $\cos\theta = \frac{1}{2}$, $\sin\theta = \frac{1}{2}\surd 3$, and the (x', y')-equation is

$$(1+\tfrac{3}{2}\surd 3)x'^2+(1-\tfrac{1}{2}\surd 3)y'^2 = 1.$$

Since $\frac{1}{2}\surd 3$ is less than 1, both coefficients are positive, and the equation in its new form is easily seen to represent an ellipse, although this was by no means obvious in its original form.

Exercises on Chapter 3

1. If the vectors **a**, **b**, **c** have components (2, 1, —1), (—3, 1, 0) and (0, 1, —2) respectively, find the components of the following vectors:

$$3\mathbf{a}+2\mathbf{b}-7\mathbf{c}, \quad 4\mathbf{a}+5\mathbf{b}, \quad 3\mathbf{b}+7\mathbf{c}, \quad \mathbf{a}+\mathbf{b}-\mathbf{c}.$$

2. Points A, B, C have coordinates (1, 1, —1), (4, 1, 2), (—2, 1, 2). Find the coordinates of the following points:

(i) the point P on AB between A and B such that AB = 3AP;
(ii) the point Q on BA produced such that AB = 3AQ;
(iii) the midpoint of CQ;
(iv) the centroid of the triangle ABC.

3. The points A, B, C have coordinates

$$A(-1, 4, 3), \quad B(2, -1, 0), \quad C(5, 2, -3).$$

A point P lies on BC between B and C so that 2BP = PC. A point Q is chosen on AP between A and P so that AQ = $\frac{1}{4}$AP. Find the coordinates of P and Q and prove that the angle PBQ is a right angle.

4. If **a** = (1, 2, 0), **b** = (0, 1, 2), **c** = (1, 0, —1), find numbers p, q, r such that $p\mathbf{a}+q\mathbf{b}+r\mathbf{c} = (1, 1, 1)$.

5. By applying Pythagoras's theorem to the right-angled triangle with vector sides $\mathbf{a} = (a_1, a_2, a_3)$, and $\mathbf{b} = (b_1, b_2, b_3)$ and $\mathbf{a}+\mathbf{b}$, show that, if the directions of **a** and **b** are right angles, then

$$a_1b_1+a_2b_2+a_3b_3 = 0.$$

(Another proof of this important formula is given in Chapter 4.)

6. Which of the following sets of three points are collinear?

(i) (1, —2, 5), (2, —4, 4), (—1, 2, 7);
(ii) (3, 6, 1), (9, 9, 2), (1, 5, $\frac{2}{3}$);
(iii) (5, 1, 7), (3, —1, 1), (6, 2, 11).

In those cases where the points are collinear (if any), find the ratio in which the second point divides the segment defined by the first and the third.

7. Using the condition in Question 5, show that the vectors

$$\mathbf{v}_1 = (\tfrac{2}{3}, \tfrac{2}{3}, -\tfrac{1}{3}), \quad \mathbf{v}_2 = (\tfrac{2}{3}, -\tfrac{1}{3}, \tfrac{2}{3}), \quad \mathbf{v}_3 = (-\tfrac{1}{3}, \tfrac{2}{3}, \tfrac{2}{3})$$

are three mutually perpendicular unit vectors. What are the components, relative to the base $\mathbf{v}_1$, $\mathbf{v}_2$, $\mathbf{v}_3$ of the vector (3, 2, 7)?

8. The vertices of a triangle are A(3, 1, 1), B(1, 0, —1), C(4, —3, 2). M is the point dividing BC internally so that BM = $\frac{1}{2}$MC. Show that AM is perpendicular to BC.

9. Points A, B, C in the plane have coordinates (4, 2), (2, −4), (−1, −3) respectively. Find the coordinates of the centroid G of the triangle ABC. A new coordinate system is taken, with the same origin, but with the new axes obtained from the old by rotation through an acute angle θ such that $\cos\theta = \frac{3}{5}$. What are the coordinates of A, B, C, G in the new system?

10. In one plane coordinate system two points have coordinates (16, 9), (14, 6). After rotation of the axes through an acute angle θ, the points have coordinates (a, c) and $(b, -c)$. Find $\sin\theta$, $\cos\theta$ and the coordinates of the points in the new system.

11. A new coordinate system (x', y') is obtained by rotating an old coordinate system (x, y) through half a right angle. The origin is kept fixed. Find the new equations of the loci whose old equations are as follows.

(i) $x^2+y^2 = 1$,
(ii) $x^2+y^2+x+y+1 = 0$,
(iii) $x^2-y^2 = 3$,
(iv) $x^2+xy+y^2+3x-5y+4 = 0$.

12. Find a change of origin, axes fixed in direction so that, in the new system, the locus with old equation

$$x^2+xy+y^2-3y+5 = 0$$

should have an equation in which only terms of degree zero and two occur.

4

THE SCALAR PRODUCT

1. Introduction

In vector algebra there are three kinds of multiplication:

(1) number-vector multiplication (already defined);
(2) the scalar product;
(3) the vector product.

These three operations are of quite distinct types. In operation (1) a number and a vector are multiplied and the result is a vector. In both operations (2) and (3) two vectors are 'multiplied', but the result of operation (2) is a *number* and that of operation (3) is a *vector*. Since it is obviously essential that no confusion should arise between these operations, different symbols are used for them. The types of vector multiplication are listed in the following table.

Name	*Type*	*Symbol*
Number-vector multiplication	Number times vector = vector	None
Scalar product	Vector times vector = number	.
Vector product	Vector times vector = vector	$\times$

The scalar product is a useful means of dealing with many questions involving distance and angle. It is also useful in mechanics—the work done by a force is an example of a scalar product—and generalizations of the concept play an important part in modern algebra and analysis. The vector product, dealt with in the next chapter, is useful in the solid geometry of planes and lines. Like the scalar product, it has applications in mechanics, and its algebra is a stepping-stone to more advanced theories. Its applications and generalizations are not, perhaps, as fundamental and universal as those of the scalar product.

2. Definition of the scalar product

Definition 5a. Let $\mathbf{a}$, $\mathbf{b}$ be two non-zero vectors, θ the angle between them. Then the scalar product $\mathbf{a}.\mathbf{b}$ is defined to be the *number* $|\mathbf{a}|\,|\mathbf{b}|\cos\theta$.

Definition 5b. If either **a** or **b** is the zero vector, the scalar product $\mathbf{a}.\mathbf{b}$ is defined to be the *number* zero, that is, $\mathbf{0}.\mathbf{a} = \mathbf{a}.\mathbf{0} = 0$.

Note on the measurement of θ. The angle θ is the amount of rotation needed to bring the direction and sense of **a** into line with those of **b**. This is the method of measurement used in Chapter 3, § 3, where the projection of one vector on another was considered. Thus if $p(\mathbf{b})$ denotes the projection of **b** on **a**, we have

$$\mathbf{a}.\mathbf{b} = |\,\mathbf{a}\,|\,|\,\mathbf{b}\,|\cos\theta = |\,\mathbf{a}\,|\,p(\mathbf{b}). \tag{1}$$

That is: *the scalar product of two non-zero vectors is equal to the length of one vector multiplied by the projection of the other upon it.*

3. Immediate consequences of the definition

(i) The condition for two non-zero vectors to be at right angles is that $\cos\theta = 0$, or $\mathbf{a}.\mathbf{b} = |\,\mathbf{a}\,|\,|\,\mathbf{b}\,|\cos\theta = 0.$ (2)

(ii)
$$\mathbf{a}.\mathbf{a} = |\,\mathbf{a}\,|\,|\,\mathbf{a}\,|\cos 0 = |\,\mathbf{a}\,|^2. \tag{3}$$

(iii) The components (a_1, a_2, a_3) of a vector **a** relative to the base $\mathbf{u}_1, \mathbf{u}_2, \mathbf{u}_3$ are the projections of **a** upon $\mathbf{u}_1, \mathbf{u}_2, \mathbf{u}_3$ respectively. Since the base-vectors are unit vectors, we have, by (1)

$$a_1 = \mathbf{a}.\mathbf{u}_1, \quad a_2 = \mathbf{a}.\mathbf{u}_2, \quad a_3 = \mathbf{a}.\mathbf{u}_3\,. \tag{4}$$

(iv)
$$\mathbf{a}.\mathbf{b} = \mathbf{b}.\mathbf{a}. \tag{5}$$

4. The distributive laws

In this section the following *distributive laws* are proved.

$$\mathbf{a}.(\mathbf{b}+\mathbf{c}) = \mathbf{a}.\mathbf{b}+\mathbf{a}.\mathbf{c}, \tag{6}$$

$$\mathbf{a}.(k\mathbf{b}) = k(\mathbf{a}.\mathbf{b}). \tag{7}$$

The reader should be quite sure that he understands the meaning of these formulae. In (6), for instance, the sign + is used with two meanings; on the left of the equation it denotes vector addition, on the right number addition (the sum of the two numbers $\mathbf{a}.\mathbf{b}$, $\mathbf{a}.\mathbf{c}$). In (7) three different kinds of multiplication occur, the scalar product, denoted by . , number-vector multiplication ($k\mathbf{b}$), and, on the right, the ordinary multiplication of numbers (the number k multiplied by the *number* $\mathbf{a}.\mathbf{b}$).

If $\mathbf{a} = \mathbf{0}$, both sides of both equations (6), (7) reduce to zero. We need only prove the formulae, therefore, on the assumption that $\mathbf{a} \neq \mathbf{0}$. The proof depends on formula (1) and the properties of projections.

Proof of (*6*), (*7*). As above, let $p(\mathbf{a})$ denote the operation of projection on the vector **a**. By Chapter 3, § 4,

$$p(\mathbf{b}+\mathbf{c}) = p(\mathbf{b})+p(\mathbf{c}), \qquad p(k\mathbf{b}) = kp(\mathbf{b}).$$

Multiply by the number $|\mathbf{a}|$, and apply the formula (1). We deduce

$$\mathbf{a}.(\mathbf{b}+\mathbf{c}) = \mathbf{a}.\mathbf{b}+\mathbf{a}.\mathbf{c}, \qquad \mathbf{a}.(k\mathbf{b}) = k(\mathbf{a}.\mathbf{b}),$$

as desired.

5. Formula in terms of components

Let $\mathbf{a} = (a_1, a_2, a_3)$, $\mathbf{b} = (b_1, b_2, b_3)$. We wish to find the value of $\mathbf{a}.\mathbf{b}$. By the distributive laws (6), (7) we have

$$\begin{aligned}\mathbf{a}.\mathbf{b} &= \mathbf{a}.(b_1\mathbf{u}_1+b_2\mathbf{u}_2+b_3\mathbf{u}_3)\\ &= b_1(\mathbf{a}.\mathbf{u}_1)+b_2(\mathbf{a}.\mathbf{u}_2)+b_3(\mathbf{a}.\mathbf{u}_3),\end{aligned}$$

so, by (4), $$\mathbf{a}.\mathbf{b} = a_1b_1+a_2b_2+a_3b_3. \tag{8}$$

If $\mathbf{b} = \mathbf{a}$, this reduces to the formula (using (3))

$$|\mathbf{a}|^2 = a_1^2+a_2^2+a_3^2,$$

already found by another method.

6. Consequences of the formulae

Because of the distributive and commutative laws (5) and (6), it is possible to expand the scalar product of two sums of vectors term by term. Thus

$$\begin{aligned}(\mathbf{a}+\mathbf{b}).(\mathbf{c}+\mathbf{d}) &= (\mathbf{a}+\mathbf{b}).\mathbf{c}+(\mathbf{a}+\mathbf{b}).\mathbf{d}\\ &= \mathbf{a}.\mathbf{c}+\mathbf{b}.\mathbf{c}+\mathbf{a}.\mathbf{d}+\mathbf{b}.\mathbf{d}. \qquad (9)\end{aligned}$$

Putting $\mathbf{c} = \mathbf{a}$, $\mathbf{d} = -\mathbf{b}$, this becomes

$$(\mathbf{a}+\mathbf{b}).(\mathbf{a}-\mathbf{b}) = |\mathbf{a}|^2-|\mathbf{b}|^2.$$

This formula shows that if $|\mathbf{a}| = |\mathbf{b}|$, then $\mathbf{a}+\mathbf{b}$ is at right angles to $\mathbf{a}-\mathbf{b}$, by (2). In other words, the diagonals of a rhombus are perpendicular—the fact required in Chapter 2, § 8. If, instead, we put $\mathbf{c} = \mathbf{a}$, $\mathbf{d} = \mathbf{b}$ in (9), we obtain the formula

$$|\mathbf{a}+\mathbf{b}|^2 = |\mathbf{a}|^2+|\mathbf{b}|^2+2\mathbf{a}.\mathbf{b}.$$

This is the vector form of the 'cosine rule' in trigonometry, for if **a**, **b** represent two sides of a triangle, $\mathbf{a}+\mathbf{b}$ represents the third side and $\mathbf{a}.\mathbf{b}$ is the product of the lengths of the two sides with the cosine of the exterior angle at the vertex common to the two sides. It is the exterior angle, because one of the vectors has a sense directed towards the vertex and the other is directed away from it. This accounts for the plus sign in the formula. In the trigonometrical form an interior angle is normally taken and the sign is minus.

7. Geometrical illustrations

Example 1. The orthocentre property. The use of the scalar product gives a very short proof of the orthocentre property of a triangle. Let ABC be a triangle and let H be the intersection of the altitudes through A, B. Then HA is perpendicular to BC and HB is perpendicular to CA. We have to prove that the third altitude also passes through H, or, in other words, that HC is perpendicular to AB. Take H as origin and let A, B, C have position vectors **a, b, c** respectively. Using condition (2) for perpendicularity, we have $\overrightarrow{HA}.\overrightarrow{BC} = 0$, that is $\mathbf{a}.(\mathbf{c}-\mathbf{b}) = 0$, so $\mathbf{a}.\mathbf{b} = \mathbf{a}.\mathbf{c}$. Similarly, since HB is an altitude, $\mathbf{b}.\mathbf{c} = \mathbf{b}.\mathbf{a}$. Hence $\mathbf{b}.\mathbf{c} = \mathbf{a}.\mathbf{c}$, so $(\mathbf{b}-\mathbf{a}).\mathbf{c} = 0$, and HC is perpendicular to AB as required.

Example 2. Let G be the centroid of a triangle ABC and let X be any point. Show that

$$XA^2+XB^2+XC^2 = 3XG^2+GA^2+GB^2+GC^2.$$

This result is most simply proved by taking G as origin and letting A, B, C, X have position vectors **a, b, c, x.** Since the centroid has position vector $\frac{1}{3}(\mathbf{a}+\mathbf{b}+\mathbf{c})$, it follows, when the centroid is the origin, that $\mathbf{a}+\mathbf{b}+\mathbf{c} = \mathbf{0}$. We have

$$\begin{aligned} & XA^2+XB^2+XC^2 \\ &= |\mathbf{x}-\mathbf{a}|^2+|\mathbf{x}-\mathbf{b}|^2+|\mathbf{x}-\mathbf{c}|^2 \\ &= |\mathbf{x}|^2-2\mathbf{a}.\mathbf{x}+|\mathbf{a}|^2+|\mathbf{x}|^2-2\mathbf{b}.\mathbf{x} \\ &\qquad +|\mathbf{b}|^2+|\mathbf{x}|^2-2\mathbf{c}.\mathbf{x}+|\mathbf{c}|^2 \\ &= 3|\mathbf{x}|^2-2(\mathbf{a}+\mathbf{b}+\mathbf{c}).\mathbf{x}+|\mathbf{a}|^2+|\mathbf{b}|^2+|\mathbf{c}|^2. \end{aligned}$$

Now $\mathbf{a}+\mathbf{b}+\mathbf{c} = \mathbf{0}$, so the second term vanishes, and our expression is $3|\mathbf{x}|^2+|\mathbf{a}|^2+|\mathbf{b}|^2+|\mathbf{c}|^2$, as was to be proved.

Questions involving distance and perpendicularity can often be solved by using scalar products. The method of attack is straightforward. First choose an origin and name the position vectors of the various points. Next write down as vector equations the conditions given and the result to be proved. Straightforward algebra usually enables us to deduce the result from the given conditions.

A good choice of origin may simplify the algebra. For instance, in the example above on the orthocentre, H is the obvious choice of origin, since any other choice would destroy the symmetry between A, B, C. In the second example, X or G should, for the same reason, be chosen as origin in preference to A, B, or C. In some ways, X might appear to be a more natural choice than G. The reader may find it interesting, as a comparison, to solve the problem using X as origin.

8. Angle between two vectors. Numerical examples

If neither **a** nor **b** is the zero vector, and if θ is the angle between **a** and **b**, then θ may often be calculated from the formula

$$\cos\theta = \frac{\mathbf{a}.\mathbf{b}}{|\mathbf{a}|\,|\mathbf{b}|}.$$

This formula is very useful in coordinate geometry. A few examples will illustrate its importance.

Example 1. If $\mathbf{a} = (5, 3, 7)$, $\mathbf{b} = (2, -8, 4)$, find the angle between **a** and **b**.

The first step is to evaluate the scalar product **a.b** using formula (8). This is conveniently done by writing the vectors one under the other, multiplying corresponding components, and adding the products, thus:

$$\begin{aligned} \mathbf{a} &= (5, 3, 7) \\ \mathbf{b} &= (2, -8, 4) \\ \mathbf{a}.\mathbf{b} &= 10-24+28 = 14. \end{aligned}$$

Since, by Pythagoras's theorem, $a = \sqrt{83}$, $b = \sqrt{84} = 2\sqrt{21}$, we deduce from (10) that $\cos\theta = 7/\sqrt{(83.21)}$. (If a numerical answer is needed, $\cos\theta$ can now be calculated to a suitable degree of accuracy and θ read off from trigonometrical tables.)

Example 2. Find the lengths of the sides, cosines of the angles, and the area of the triangle with vertices

$$A(3, -1, 4), \quad B(2, -2, 1), \quad C(5, 1, 3).$$

By subtraction, we find $\overrightarrow{AB} = (-1, -1, -3)$, $\overrightarrow{AC} = (2, 2, -1)$, so $AB = \sqrt{11}$, $AC = 3$, and by (8) $\overrightarrow{AB}.\overrightarrow{AC} = -2-2+3 = -1$.

Using (10), $\cos A = -\dfrac{1}{3\sqrt{11}}$. Since $\sin^2 A+\cos^2 A = 1$, $\sin A = \sqrt{\dfrac{98}{99}} = \dfrac{7\sqrt{2}}{3\sqrt{11}}$. Area $= \frac{1}{2}$AB AC $\sin A = 7\sqrt{2}/2$.

Another method of finding the area of a triangle will be explained in Chapter 5.

Example 3. Find a unit vector which makes an angle of 45° with the vector $\mathbf{a} = (2, 2, -1)$ and an angle of 60° with $\mathbf{b} = (0, 1, -1)$.

Let the unknown vector be $\mathbf{u} = (x, y, z)$. We shall require three equations to determine the three unknowns. These are:

(i) $\mathbf{u}$ is a unit vector:

$$x^2+y^2+z^2 = 1.$$

(ii) $\mathbf{u}$ makes 45° angle with $\mathbf{a}$, so $\mathbf{u}.\mathbf{a} = |\mathbf{u}||\mathbf{a}|\cos 45°$, or

$$2x+2y-z = \frac{3}{\sqrt{2}}.$$

(iii) $\mathbf{u}$ makes 60° angle with $\mathbf{b}$, so $\mathbf{u}.\mathbf{b} = |\mathbf{u}||\mathbf{b}|\cos 60°$, or

$$y-z = \frac{1}{\sqrt{2}}.$$

The problem has been reduced to one of pure number-algebra: three equations in three unknowns. Solve equations (ii) and (iii) for y and z in terms of x, finding

(iv) $\quad y = -2x+\sqrt{2}, \qquad z = -2x+\frac{1}{2}\sqrt{2}.$

Substitute for y, z in equation (i), obtaining the quadratic in x:

$$9x^2-6\sqrt{2}x+\frac{3}{2} = 0,$$

with roots $x = 1/\sqrt{2}$, $1/3\sqrt{2}$. Once x is known, y and z are determined by equations (iv). There are, therefore, two solutions of the problem,

$$\mathbf{u} = \left(\frac{1}{\sqrt{2}}, 0, -\frac{1}{\sqrt{2}}\right), \qquad \mathbf{u} = \left(\frac{1}{3\sqrt{2}}, \frac{4}{3\sqrt{2}}, \frac{1}{3\sqrt{2}}\right).$$

9. Trigonometrical application

As in Chapter 3, § 10, we may restrict consideration to vectors in a fixed plane, so that each vector has two components. By exactly the same arguments as were used earlier in this chapter, the scalar product of (a, b) with (c, d) is $ac+bd$. As an application of this consider two unit vectors $\mathbf{a} = [1, \theta]$, $\mathbf{b} = [1, \phi]$. (See Fig. 18 in Chapter 3, § 10.) Clearly the angle between them is $\theta-\phi$, and, since the vectors are unit vectors,

$$\mathbf{a}.\mathbf{b} = \cos(\theta-\phi).$$

On the other hand,

$$\mathbf{a} = (\cos\theta, \sin\theta),$$
$$\mathbf{b} = (\cos\phi, \sin\phi),$$

so, by the formula,

$$\mathbf{a}.\mathbf{b} = \cos\theta\cos\phi+\sin\theta\sin\phi.$$

Comparing the two expressions for $\mathbf{a}.\mathbf{b}$, we have a new proof of the trigonometrical formula,

$$\cos(\theta-\phi) = \cos\theta\cos\phi+\sin\theta\sin\phi.$$

This method of proof, besides being simple in itself, gives one an easy way of remembering the sign in the formula. The angle between the two vectors is the *difference* of the two angles, but the formula for the scalar product involves a *plus* sign.

10. General remarks

Since the scalar product of two vectors is a number, one cannot expect the analogy between the scalar product and products of numbers to be very close. For instance, $\mathbf{b}.\mathbf{c}$ is itself a number, so the expression $\mathbf{a}.(\mathbf{b}.\mathbf{c})$ has *no meaning*, and there is no question of any associative law for scalar products. It is also impossible to associate a division operation with the scalar product, and cancellation of a vector from both sides of an equation involving scalar products is not permissible. Thus, if $\mathbf{a}.\mathbf{b} = \mathbf{a}.\mathbf{c}$, the vector $\mathbf{b}$ need not be equal to the vector $\mathbf{c}$. For instance, the equation $\mathbf{a}.\mathbf{b} = \mathbf{a}.\mathbf{c}$ occurs in the proof of the orthocentre property of a triangle given in § 7, certainly without any need to assume that the vertices of the triangle coincide. If you prefer a numerical example, take

$$\mathbf{a} = (1, 0, 0), \quad \mathbf{b} = (1, 2, 1), \quad \mathbf{c} = (1, -3, -2).$$

Exercises on Chapter 4

1. Find two vectors of unit length which make an angle of 45° with (1, 0, 0) and are perpendicular to the vector (0, 0, 1).

2. Find the two unit vectors which make an angle of 60° with both the vectors (1, −1, 0) and (1, 0, −1). Find also the vectors which make angles of 45° with both the above vectors.

3. Find the components of the two unit vectors which make an angle of 45 degrees with (−1, 0, 1) and an angle of 60 degrees with (−2, 2, 1). Show that these two unit vectors are perpendicular.

4. The position vectors of the vertices of a triangle are **0**, **a**, **b**. Show that its area A is given by the formula

$$4A^2 = |\mathbf{a}|^2 |\mathbf{b}|^2 - (\mathbf{a}.\mathbf{b})^2.$$

5. ABCD is a tetrahedron. Show that if the edge AB is perpendicular to the edge CD, and if also the edge AC is perpendicular to the edge BD, then the edge AD is perpendicular to the edge BC.

6. Prove that in any parallelogram the sum of the squares on the diagonals is equal to twice the sum of the squares on two adjacent sides.

7. The sum of the squares on the six edges of any tetrahedron is equal to four times the sum of the squares on the three segments joining pairs of midpoints of opposite edges.

8. If O is the circumcentre of the triangle ABC, and R is the radius of the circumcircle, express the scalar products, in pairs, of the vectors $\overrightarrow{OA}$, $\overrightarrow{OB}$, $\overrightarrow{OC}$ in terms of R and the trigonometric functions of the angles A, B, C. Deduce that

$$bc \cos A = R^2(1-\cos 2B-\cos 2C+\cos 2A).$$

9. If H is the orthocentre of the triangle in Question 8, show that

$$\overrightarrow{OH}^2 = 3R^2+2R^2(\cos 2A+\cos 2B+\cos 2C).$$

(Use the formula of Chapter 2, § 8.)

10. Three vectors **a**, **b**, **p** are given. Determine the numbers k, l, in terms of their scalar products, in such a way that the vector

$$\mathbf{p}-k\mathbf{a}-l\mathbf{b}$$

should be perpendicular to both **a** and **b**.

11. Four points O, A, B, C are given in space, each of the vectors $\overrightarrow{OA} = \mathbf{a}$, $\overrightarrow{OB} = \mathbf{b}$, $\overrightarrow{OC} = \mathbf{c}$ having unit length. The angles BOC, COA, AOB are denoted by α, β, γ. M is the midpoint of BC. Express the vectors $\overrightarrow{CA}$, $\overrightarrow{AB}$, $\overrightarrow{OM}$, $\overrightarrow{AM}$ in terms of **a**, **b**, **c**. Show that, if one of the angles BAC, OMA is a right angle, so is the other, and that the condition for these two angles to be right angles is

$$1+\cos\alpha = \cos\beta+\cos\gamma.$$

12. Which of the following expressions represent vectors and which represent numbers?

(i) $\mathbf{b}.\mathbf{c}+\mathbf{c}.\mathbf{a}+\mathbf{a}.\mathbf{b}$, (ii) $(\mathbf{b}.\mathbf{c})\mathbf{a}+(\mathbf{c}.\mathbf{a})\mathbf{b}+(\mathbf{a}.\mathbf{b})\mathbf{c}$, (iii) $(\mathbf{b}.\mathbf{c})(\mathbf{c}.\mathbf{a})\mathbf{a}$, (iv) $[(\mathbf{b}.\mathbf{c})\mathbf{c}+(\mathbf{b}.\mathbf{a})\mathbf{a}].(\mathbf{b}+2\mathbf{a})$.

Evaluate these when $\mathbf{a} = (1, 0, 1)$, $\mathbf{b} = (1, 1, 2)$, $\mathbf{c} = (0, 2, 1)$.

13. Three points A, B, C have coordinates A(1, 6, −2), B(2, 5, 4), C(4, 6, −3). Find the lengths of the sides, cosines of the angles and area of the triangle ABC.

14. The angles between the non-zero vectors $\mathbf{b}$ and $\mathbf{c}$, $\mathbf{c}$ and $\mathbf{a}$, $\mathbf{a}$ and $\mathbf{b}$ are α, β, γ respectively. The vectors $\mathbf{u}$ and $\mathbf{v}$ are defined as follows.

$$\mathbf{u} = (\mathbf{a}.\mathbf{c})\mathbf{b}-(\mathbf{a}.\mathbf{b})\mathbf{c}, \qquad \mathbf{v} = (\mathbf{a}.\mathbf{c})\mathbf{b}-(\mathbf{b}.\mathbf{c})\mathbf{a}.$$

Show that if $\mathbf{u}$ and $\mathbf{v}$ are perpendicular, then

$$\cos^2\beta = \cos\alpha\cos\beta\cos\gamma.$$

15. All the edges of a tetrahedron OABC are of the same length. G is the centroid of the triangle ABC, and P is the midpoint of OG. Show that PA, PB, PC are mutually perpendicular.

16. The four vertices of a tetrahedron have coordinates

$$(0, 0, 0), \quad (8, 2, 2), \quad (5, -4, 2), \quad (5, 2, -4).$$

Show that the areas of all four faces are equal.

5

THE VECTOR PRODUCT

1. Introduction

It is often necessary to find a vector which is perpendicular to each of two given vectors. There are, of course, many such vectors, and it is most useful to choose one whose length is the product of the lengths of the original vectors multiplied by the sine of the angle between them. This product has its uses in mechanics, for instance when dealing with moments of forces and with angular velocity. Regarded from an algebraic viewpoint, it has a close connexion with the method of cross-multiplication in dealing with linear equations.

2. Left- and right-handed system of three vectors

Let **a**, **b** and **c** be three non-zero, non-coplanar vectors, represented by segments $\overrightarrow{OA}$, $\overrightarrow{OB}$, $\overrightarrow{OC}$ with a common initial point O. The least angular rotation which moves $\overrightarrow{OA}$ to coincide in direction and sense with $\overrightarrow{OB}$ will appear clockwise to an observer on one side of the plane OAB, but anticlockwise to an observer on the other side. If an observer at C sees the rotation as anticlockwise, the system [**a**, **b**, **c**] is called a *right-handed system*. Otherwise, if the observer at C sees the rotation as clockwise, the system [**a**, **b**, **c**] is called a *left-handed system*. Clearly, if [**a**, **b**, **c**] is right-handed, then [**a**, **b**, −**c**] is left-handed, and conversely. What is more, the order in which the vectors are written plays a part. If [**a**, **b**, **c**] is right-handed, the systems [**b**, **c**, **a**], [**c**, **a**, **b**] obtained from it by cyclic interchange are also right-handed, but the systems [**b**, **a**, **c**], [**c**, **b**, **a**], [**a**, **c**, **b**] obtained by interchanging a pair are left-handed. In Fig. 19, the vectors **a**, **b** are shown in the plane of the paper. Since the idea of right- and left-handed systems is essentially three-dimensional, it is impossible to draw a plane picture which illustrates it accurately, so the vector **c** cannot lie in the plane of the paper and is not drawn in; but if the vector **c** is directed *away* from the reader, into the plane of the paper, then [**a**, **b**, **c**] is a right-handed system, whereas if the vector **c** is *pointing at* the reader, out of the plane of the paper, then the system is left-handed. Another way of picturing the situation is to consider an ordinary right-handed screw. If **a** and **b** are vectors in the plane perpendicular to the axis of the screw and **c** is directed along the axis of the screw, then [**a**, **b**, **c**] is right-handed if, on rotating the

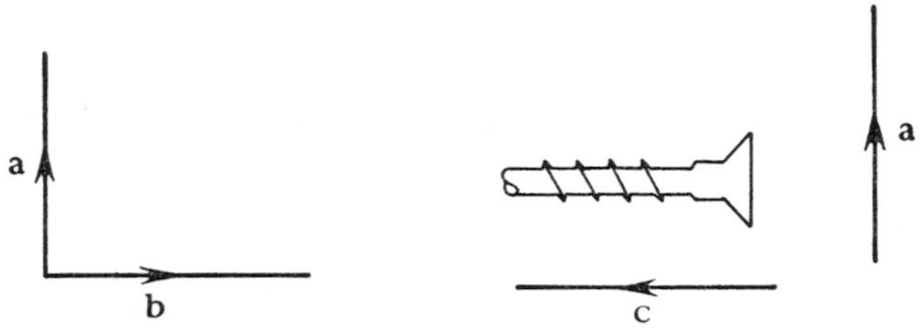

FIG. 19

(i) **c** into paper, right-handed; **c** out of paper, left-handed.

(ii) **b** into paper for right-handed system.

screwdriver from **a** to **b**, one is forcing the screw in the sense given by **c**.

Until now it has not been necessary to consider whether the system [$\mathbf{u}_1$, $\mathbf{u}_2$, $\mathbf{u}_3$] of base-vectors is left-handed or right-handed. All the formulae for addition, number-vector multiplication and scalar products, are the same in both types of coordinate system. This is not true of the formula for the vector product. We assume in what follows that *the base-vectors form a right-handed system.*

3. The vector product

Definition 6a. Let **a**, **b** be two non-zero vectors, not both parallel and let θ be the angle between them. The vector product $\mathbf{a} \times \mathbf{b}$ is a *vector* defined as follows.

Magnitude: $|\mathbf{a}||\mathbf{b}||\sin\theta|$.
Direction: perpendicular to both **a** and **b**.
Sense: so that [**a**, **b**, $\mathbf{a} \times \mathbf{b}$] forms a right-handed system.

Definition 6b. If either **a** or **b** is the zero vector or if **a** is parallel to **b** then $\mathbf{a} \times \mathbf{b} = \mathbf{0}$.

It is necessary to give a separate treatment of the cases covered by Definition 6b because in these cases the second and third parts of Definition 6a either do not make sense or else do not give a unique direction and sense; but Definition 6b is the only possibility consistent with the first part of Definition 6a, which implies that the vector product should be zero if either **a** or **b** is the zero vector or if $\sin\theta$ is zero.

Note 1. The magnitude of $\mathbf{a}\times\mathbf{b}$ is the area of the parallelogram with vector sides **a** and **b**. Therefore $\mathbf{a}\times\mathbf{b}$ is sometimes referred to as the *vector area* of the parallelogram.

Note 2. If [**a**, **b**, **c**] is right-handed, then [**b**, **a**, **c**] is left-handed, so [**b**, **a**, −**c**] is right-handed again, by § 2. Hence, in particular [**b**, **a**, $\mathbf{a}\times\mathbf{b}$] is a left-handed system, so we have, in contrast to number-algebra,

$$\mathbf{a}\times\mathbf{b} = -(\mathbf{b}\times\mathbf{a}). \tag{1}$$

Note 3. If [**a**, **b**, **c**] is right-handed, then [−**a**, **b**, **c**] is left-handed, so [−**a**, **b**, −**c**] is right-handed. It follows that

$$(-\mathbf{a})\times\mathbf{b} = -(\mathbf{a}\times\mathbf{b}). \tag{2}$$

It is clear, directly from the definition, that if k is positive,

$$(k\mathbf{a})\times\mathbf{b} = k(\mathbf{a}\times\mathbf{b}).$$

By (2), this is true for negative values of k as well. More generally

$$(k\mathbf{a})\times(l\mathbf{b}) = kl(\mathbf{a}\times\mathbf{b}). \tag{3}$$

Note 4. The relation $\mathbf{a}\times\mathbf{b} = 0$ holds *only* if **a** is parallel to **b** or if **a** or **b** is zero. Thus if **a** and **b** are non-zero vectors the following three statements are all equivalent.

(i) $\mathbf{a}\times\mathbf{b} = 0$,
(ii) $\mathbf{a} = k\mathbf{b}$ (for some number k), (Chapter 2, § 11)
(iii) **a** is parallel to **b**.

4. Rotation of vectors in a plane

Let Π be a plane, looked at from a point on one side of it, so that it is possible to distinguish between clockwise and anti-clockwise rotations in Π. If **a** is any vector in Π, let $\mathbf{a}_\theta$ denote the vector obtained in Π from **a** by anticlockwise rotation through an angle θ. That is, $\mathbf{a}_\theta$ is equal in magnitude to **a**, and the angle between **a** and $\mathbf{a}_\theta$, measured anticlockwise, is equal to θ.

If **a**, **b** *are any vectors in* Π, *then*

$$(\mathbf{a}+\mathbf{b})_\theta = \mathbf{a}_\theta+\mathbf{b}_\theta. \tag{4}$$

Proof. We omit the trivial cases $\mathbf{a} = \mathbf{0}$ or $\mathbf{b} = \mathbf{0}$. Let $\overrightarrow{OA}$, $\overrightarrow{OB}$

represent the vectors **a**, **b**. Complete the parallelogram BOAC, so that $\mathbf{c} = \overrightarrow{OC}$ represents the sum $\mathbf{a}+\mathbf{b}$. Let $\overrightarrow{OA'}$, $\overrightarrow{OB'}$ represent the vectors $\mathbf{a}_\theta$, $\mathbf{b}_\theta$ in order, so that the angles AOA′, BOB′ are both equal to θ, measured in an anticlockwise sense.

The triangles AOB, A′OB′ are easily seen to be congruent, since the two sides of one meeting at O are equal to the two sides of the other meeting at O and the contained angles are equal. It follows easily that the parallelograms AOBC, A′OB′C′ are congruent, $|\overrightarrow{OC}|$, $|\overrightarrow{OC'}|$ are equal, and the angle COC′ is equal to θ. Thus $\overrightarrow{OC}_\theta = \overrightarrow{OC'}$, and $(\mathbf{a}+\mathbf{b})_\theta = \overrightarrow{OC'} = \overrightarrow{OA'}+\overrightarrow{OB'} = \mathbf{a}_\theta+\mathbf{b}_\theta$.

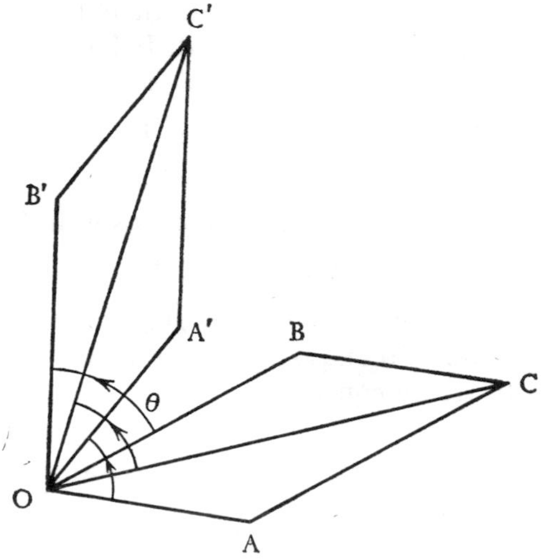

FIG. 20

5. Vector product with a fixed vector

Let $\mathbf{a} = \overrightarrow{OA}$ be a fixed non-zero vector. Let Π be the plane through O perpendicular to OA and let $\mathbf{x} = \overrightarrow{OX}$ be any vector. The operation of passing from $\mathbf{x}$ to $\mathbf{a}\times\mathbf{x}$ can be split into three operations, as follows (Fig 21).

Step 1. Replace $\mathbf{x}$ by its projection $\mathbf{x}' = \overrightarrow{OX'}$ on Π.

Step 2. Rotate $\mathbf{x}'$ through a right angle in Π in the sense which appears anticlockwise from A, to obtain $\mathbf{x}'' = \overrightarrow{OX''}$.

Step 3. Replace $\mathbf{x}''$ by $|\,\mathbf{a}\,|\,\mathbf{x}''$.

The vector $\mathbf{x}'$ has magnitude $|\,\mathbf{x}\,|\,|\sin\theta\,|$, the vector $\mathbf{x}''$, obtained from $\mathbf{x}'$ by rotation, also has magnitude $|\,\mathbf{x}\,|\,|\sin\theta\,|$, so $|\,\mathbf{a}\,|\,\mathbf{x}''$ has magnitude $|\,\mathbf{a}\,|\,|\,\mathbf{x}\,|\,|\sin\theta\,|$. In addition, $|\,\mathbf{a}\,|\,\mathbf{x}''$ is at right angles to both the vectors **a**, **x** and forms a right-handed system with them. Thus $|\,\mathbf{a}\,|\,\mathbf{x}''$, the result of the three steps indicated above, is the vector product $\mathbf{a}\times\mathbf{x}$.

The first step above is a projection, the second a rotation, and the third, multiplying the vector by a positive number, may be called an *expansion*. Thus the operation

$$\mathbf{x} \longrightarrow \mathbf{a}\times\mathbf{x}$$

has been shown to be equivalent to a succession of three operations

$$\mathbf{x} \xrightarrow{\text{P}} \mathbf{x}' \xrightarrow{\text{R}} \mathbf{x}'' \xrightarrow{\text{E}} \mathbf{a}\times\mathbf{x},$$

where P is a projection, R a rotation, E an expansion.

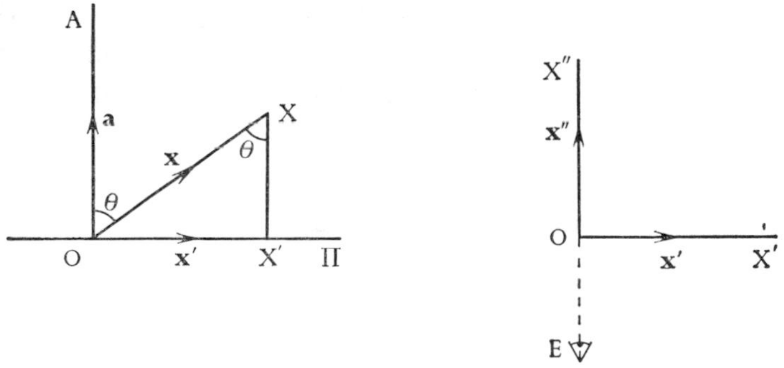

FIG. 21

(i) View to an observer at E in (ii). (ii) View of Π to an observer at A in (i).

6. The distributive laws

We now prove the *distributive law*

$$\mathbf{a}\times(\mathbf{b}+\mathbf{c}) = \mathbf{a}\times\mathbf{b}+\mathbf{a}\times\mathbf{c}. \tag{5}$$

From (5) and (1) follows also the right-handed distributive law

$$(\mathbf{b}+\mathbf{c})\times\mathbf{a} = \mathbf{b}\times\mathbf{a}+\mathbf{c}\times\mathbf{a},$$

which arises from (5) simply by changing signs across.

Proof of (*5*). Let $\overrightarrow{\text{OA}} = \mathbf{a}$ and let Π be as in § 5. Write $\mathbf{b}+\mathbf{c} = \mathbf{d}$

and, as in § 5, let $\mathbf{b}'$, $\mathbf{c}'$, $\mathbf{d}'$ be the projections of $\mathbf{b}$, $\mathbf{c}$, $\mathbf{d}$ on Π, and let $\mathbf{b}''$, $\mathbf{c}''$, $\mathbf{d}''$ be obtained by rotating $\mathbf{b}'$, $\mathbf{c}'$, $\mathbf{d}'$ each through a right angle in Π. By the properties of projections (Chapter 3, § 4), we see that $\mathbf{b}'+\mathbf{c}' = \mathbf{d}'$, and by the property of rotations (§ 4 above) it then follows that $\mathbf{b}''+\mathbf{c}'' = \mathbf{d}''$. Hence, by formula (8), Chapter 2, $|\,\mathbf{a}\,|\,\mathbf{b}''+|\,\mathbf{a}\,|\,\mathbf{c}'' = |\,\mathbf{a}\,|\,\mathbf{d}''$, or, by § 5 above,

$$\mathbf{a}\times\mathbf{b}+\mathbf{a}\times\mathbf{c} = \mathbf{a}\times\mathbf{d} = \mathbf{a}\times(\mathbf{b}+\mathbf{c}).$$

This proves (5) when $\mathbf{a} \neq \mathbf{0}$. If $\mathbf{a} = \mathbf{0}$, the equation is still true because both sides reduce to zero.

7. The formula in terms of components

The formulae (3), (5) enable us to express the vector product in terms of components. The unit vectors $\mathbf{u}_1$, $\mathbf{u}_2$, $\mathbf{u}_3$ are at right angles, and form a right-handed system. Thus $\mathbf{u}_1\times\mathbf{u}_2 = \mathbf{u}_3$, $\mathbf{u}_1\times\mathbf{u}_3 = -\mathbf{u}_2$, $\mathbf{u}_2\times\mathbf{u}_1 = -\mathbf{u}_3$, $\mathbf{u}_2\times\mathbf{u}_3 = \mathbf{u}_1$, $\mathbf{u}_3\times\mathbf{u}_1 = \mathbf{u}_2$, $\mathbf{u}_3\times\mathbf{u}_2 = -\mathbf{u}_1$. This information is set out below as a multiplication table, where the left-hand vertical column gives the first factor and the top horizontal line gives the second factor in each product. (Tables of this kind have some theoretical importance in the theory of finite groups and other parts of algebra.)

	$\mathbf{u}_1$	$\mathbf{u}_2$	$\mathbf{u}_3$
$\mathbf{u}_1$	$\mathbf{0}$	$\mathbf{u}_3$	$-\mathbf{u}_2$
$\mathbf{u}_2$	$-\mathbf{u}_3$	$\mathbf{0}$	$\mathbf{u}_1$
$\mathbf{u}_3$	$\mathbf{u}_2$	$-\mathbf{u}_1$	$\mathbf{0}$

If $\mathbf{a} = (a_1, a_2, a_3)$ and $\mathbf{b} = (b_1, b_2, b_3)$, then

$$\mathbf{a}\times\mathbf{b} = (a_1\mathbf{u}_1+a_2\mathbf{u}_2+a_3\mathbf{u}_3)\times(b_1\mathbf{u}_1+b_2\mathbf{u}_2+b_3\mathbf{u}_3).$$

Writing this out fully, using the two distributive laws, we have nine terms

$$\begin{aligned} &a_1b_1(\mathbf{u}_1\times\mathbf{u}_1)+a_1b_2(\mathbf{u}_1\times\mathbf{u}_2)+a_1b_3(\mathbf{u}_1\times\mathbf{u}_3)+\\ &+a_2b_1(\mathbf{u}_2\times\mathbf{u}_1)+a_2b_2(\mathbf{u}_2\times\mathbf{u}_2)+a_2b_3(\mathbf{u}_2\times\mathbf{u}_3)+\\ &+a_3b_1(\mathbf{u}_3\times\mathbf{u}_1)+a_3b_2(\mathbf{u}_3\times\mathbf{u}_2)+a_3b_3(\mathbf{u}_3\times\mathbf{u}_3). \end{aligned}$$

Using the multiplication table above, this reduces to

$$\mathbf{a}\times\mathbf{b} = (a_2b_3-a_3b_2)\mathbf{u}_1+(a_3b_1-a_1b_3)\mathbf{u}_2+(a_1b_2-a_2b_1)\mathbf{u}_3.$$

The components of $\mathbf{a}\times\mathbf{b}$ are therefore

$$(a_2b_3-a_3b_2,\quad a_3b_1-a_1b_3,\quad a_1b_2-a_2b_1). \tag{6}$$

The following method of obtaining the components is often useful. Write down the components of the two vectors one below the other, the components of each vector being written down in cyclic order, beginning and ending with the *second*;

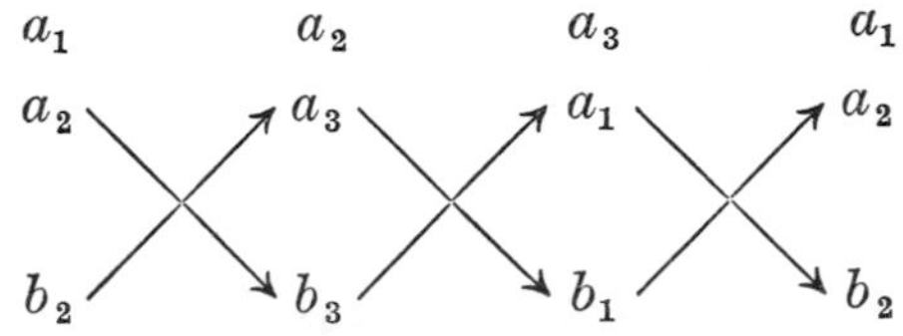

The products corresponding to a downward arrow have a plus sign, the others a minus sign.

8. Worked examples

Example 1. If $\mathbf{a} = (3, 5, 7)$, $\mathbf{b} = (1, 0, 1)$, $\mathbf{c} = (2, -1, 3)$, verify that $\mathbf{a}\times(\mathbf{b}\times\mathbf{c}) = (\mathbf{a}.\mathbf{c})\mathbf{b}-(\mathbf{a}.\mathbf{b})\mathbf{c}$.

To evaluate the left side we first obtain $\mathbf{b}\times\mathbf{c}$, using 'cross-multiplication' as in § 7.

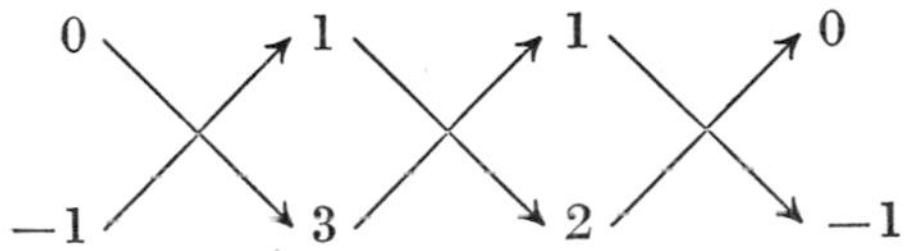

$$\mathbf{b}\times\mathbf{c} = (1, -1, -1).$$

The same process applied to the vector $\mathbf{a}$ and the vector $\mathbf{b}\times\mathbf{c}$ just found yields $\mathbf{a}\times(\mathbf{b}\times\mathbf{c}) = (2, 10, -8)$. Again, by the formulae of earlier chapters, $\mathbf{a}.\mathbf{c} = 22$, $\mathbf{a}.\mathbf{b} = 10$, so the right-hand side is $22\mathbf{b}-10\mathbf{c} = (2, 10, -8)$, and the given equation is verified.

Example 2. Find the area of the triangle with vertices

$$\text{A}(1, 3, -2),\quad \text{B}(4, 3, 0),\quad \text{C}(2, 1, 1).$$

This problem can of course be solved without the use of vector products, as we saw in the last chapter. However, the vector product gives the answer very quickly, since the area $\frac{1}{2}\text{AB AC}\sin \text{A}$ is just half the magnitude of the vector product $\overrightarrow{\text{AB}}\times\overrightarrow{\text{AC}}$. With the numbers given we have

$$\overrightarrow{\text{AB}} = (3, 0, 2),\quad \overrightarrow{\text{AC}} = (1, -2, 3),\quad \overrightarrow{\text{AB}}\times\overrightarrow{\text{AC}} = (4, -7, -6).$$

The magnitude of the last vector is $\sqrt{101}$, so the area is $\frac{1}{2}\sqrt{101}$.

Example 3. Let $\mathbf{a}$, $\mathbf{b}$, $\mathbf{c}$ be unit vectors such that $\mathbf{a}\times\mathbf{b} = \mathbf{a}\times\mathbf{c}$, and $\mathbf{b}$ makes an angle of 60 degrees with $\mathbf{c}$. Show that $\mathbf{b}-\mathbf{c} = \pm\mathbf{a}$.

Since $\mathbf{a}\times\mathbf{b} = \mathbf{a}\times\mathbf{c}$, we have $\mathbf{a}\times(\mathbf{b}-\mathbf{c}) = \mathbf{0}$, so, by § 3, Note 4, $\mathbf{b}-\mathbf{c} = k\mathbf{a}$, where k is a number. Thus

$$|\mathbf{b}-\mathbf{c}|^2 = k^2|\mathbf{a}|^2 = k^2, \quad \text{since } \mathbf{a} \text{ is a unit vector.}$$
$$k^2 = |\mathbf{b}|^2+|\mathbf{c}|^2-2\mathbf{b}.\mathbf{c}$$
$$= 2-2\cos 60^\circ = 1.$$

Thus
$$k = \pm 1, \quad \mathbf{b}-\mathbf{c} = k\mathbf{a} = \pm\mathbf{a}.$$

The principle used in Example 3, that if $\mathbf{p}\times\mathbf{q}$ vanishes then $\mathbf{p} = k\mathbf{q}$ (unless one of $\mathbf{p}$, $\mathbf{q}$ is zero), is very important. We illustrate its use by another example.

Example 4. If $\mathbf{b}\times\mathbf{c} = \mathbf{c}\times\mathbf{a} = \mathbf{a}\times\mathbf{b} \neq \mathbf{0}$, show that

$$\mathbf{a}+\mathbf{b}+\mathbf{c} = \mathbf{0}.$$

Proof. From $\mathbf{b}\times\mathbf{c} = \mathbf{c}\times\mathbf{a} = -\mathbf{a}\times\mathbf{c}$, we deduce $(\mathbf{b}+\mathbf{a})\times\mathbf{c} = \mathbf{0}$, so $\mathbf{b}+\mathbf{a} = k\mathbf{c}$. Multiply (vector product) both sides of the last equation by $\mathbf{a}$:

$$\mathbf{b}\times\mathbf{a}+\mathbf{0} = k(\mathbf{c}\times\mathbf{a}).$$

But it is given that $\mathbf{b}\times\mathbf{a} = -(\mathbf{a}\times\mathbf{b}) = -(\mathbf{c}\times\mathbf{a})$.

Thus
$$k = -1, \quad \mathbf{b}+\mathbf{a} = -\mathbf{c}, \quad \text{and} \quad \mathbf{a}+\mathbf{b}+\mathbf{c} = \mathbf{0}.$$

The statement in Example 4 is false if we do not require the three equal vector products to be different from zero. Thus, if $\mathbf{a} = \mathbf{b} = \mathbf{c} \neq \mathbf{0}$, all the other hypotheses are satisfied but not the conclusion. At what points in the argument was the assumption $\mathbf{a}\times\mathbf{b} \neq \mathbf{0}$ used implicitly?

9. Cross-multiplication

Very often in algebra it is necessary to deal with two homogeneous equations in three unknowns, for instance

$$\left.\begin{aligned} a_1x_1+a_2x_2+a_3x_3 &= 0, \\ b_1x_1+b_2x_2+b_3x_3 &= 0. \end{aligned}\right\} \qquad (7)$$

If we multiply the first equation by b_1, the second by a_1, subtract and simplify, we obtain

$$\frac{x_2}{a_3b_1-a_1b_3} = \frac{x_3}{a_1b_2-a_2b_1}.$$

Combining this with the similar equation obtained by eliminating

x_3 between the equations, we derive

$$\frac{x_1}{a_2b_3-a_3b_2} = \frac{x_2}{a_3b_1-a_1b_3} = \frac{x_3}{a_1b_2-a_2b_1} = k, \tag{8}$$

where k is a number.

Now look at the denominators in equations (8). Obviously they are obtained in the same way as the components of a vector product; so let us reconsider equations (7) and (8) in terms of vectors **a**, **b** and **x** whose components, in a certain fixed coordinate system, are (a_1, a_2, a_3), (b_1, b_2, b_3) and (x_1, x_2, x_3): Equations (7) say $\mathbf{a}.\mathbf{x} = \mathbf{b}.\mathbf{x} = 0$, in other words **x** is perpendicular to both **a** and **b**. Equations (8) say that $\mathbf{x} = k(\mathbf{a}\times\mathbf{b})$, in other words **x** is parallel to the vector product. Thus the formula 8 can be established either by a geometric or by an algebraic argument. The algebraic form of this is sometimes useful in elimination problems.

To avoid complication in the above argument, we have not considered the possibility of the denominators in (8) being zero. If all are zero, then $\mathbf{a}\times\mathbf{b} = \mathbf{0}$, **a** is parallel to **b**, and the equations (7) do not determine the direction of the vector **x**. If some, but not all, are zero, the argument has to be modified because division by zero is never admissible, but equations (8) remain true in the modified form $\mathbf{x} = k(\mathbf{a}\times\mathbf{b})$. (It is also possible to interpret equations (8) using the convention that 0/0 can take any value, as indicated at Chapter 3, § 8, Example 3. The reader is not advised to use this convention in his own working at this stage, but he must be familiar with it if he is to read standard texts on Euclidean and projective analytical geometry.)

10. The vector triple product

Another result which is not so obvious geometrically can be proved by the method of elimination. In this case we begin with the non-homogeneous equations, writing the component and the vector form of the equations side by side.

$$a_1x_1+a_2x_2+a_3x_3 = k, \qquad \mathbf{a}.\mathbf{x} = k,$$
$$b_1x_1+b_2x_2+b_3x_3 = l, \qquad \mathbf{b}.\mathbf{x} = l.$$

Let us eliminate x_1 between these equations, as before, multiplying the first equation by b_1, the second by a_1, and subtracting.

We derive

$$(a_3b_1-a_1b_3)x_3+(a_2b_1-a_1b_2)x_2 = kb_1-la_1.$$

As in § 9, the coefficients of x_3, x_2 on the left remind us of the components of the vector product $\mathbf{a}\times\mathbf{b}$. In fact, if we let $\mathbf{d} = \mathbf{a}\times\mathbf{b}$, and denote its components by (d_1, d_2, d_3), the above equation can be rewritten

$$d_2x_3-d_3x_2 = kb_1-la_1. \tag{9}$$

There is no special reason why the component x_1 should be given particular consideration. If we eliminate x_2 between our first two equations, we derive

$$d_3x_1-d_1x_3 = kb_2-la_2, \tag{10}$$

and if we eliminate x_3, we derive

$$d_1x_2-d_2x_1 = kb_3-la_3. \tag{11}$$

Now look at the equations (9), (10) and (11). Once again, they remind us of the components of a vector product, this time the product $\mathbf{d}\times\mathbf{x}$. What about the right-hand sides? A moment's study will show that the right-hand sides of (9), (10) and (11) are, in order, the three components of the vector $k\mathbf{b}-l\mathbf{a}$. Thus these three equations are the component form of the vector equation

$$\mathbf{d}\times\mathbf{x} = k\mathbf{b}-l\mathbf{a}. \tag{12}$$

The short and simple form of the equation (12), replacing the three longer equations (9), (10) and (11), illustrates the brevity of notation which we have already mentioned. It shows that vector algebra can save a bit of writing, if it does nothing else!

If, in Equation (12), we remember that $\mathbf{d}$ was introduced to denote $\mathbf{a}\times\mathbf{b}$, and that k and l are, by the equations from which we started, the scalar products $\mathbf{a}.\mathbf{x}$ and $\mathbf{b}.\mathbf{x}$, we can transform (12) into the *vector triple product identity*

$$(\mathbf{a}\times\mathbf{b})\times\mathbf{x} = (\mathbf{a}.\mathbf{x})\mathbf{b}-(\mathbf{b}.\mathbf{x})\mathbf{a}, \tag{13}$$

valid for any three vectors $\mathbf{a}$, $\mathbf{b}$ and $\mathbf{x}$. This formula has some applications in spherical trigonometry, as we shall see in Chapter 7.

11. The scalar triple product

A *parallelepiped* is the natural generalization to three dimensions of the parallelogram in the plane. It is the part of solid space cut off by three pairs of parallel planes—like a cube, but with the angles not necessarily right angles and the edges not equal. It has six faces, eight vertices and twelve edges. In Fig. 22 we illustrate a parallelepiped with vertices O,B,C,D, A,B′,C′,D′. Every edge is equal and parallel to one of the three $\overrightarrow{OA}$, $\overrightarrow{OB}$, $\overrightarrow{OC}$, and we say that the parallelepiped has *vector edges* $\overrightarrow{OA}$, $\overrightarrow{OB}$, $\overrightarrow{OC}$.

It is convenient to pick one of the plane faces and call it a *base*. The perpendicular distance between the base and the plane face

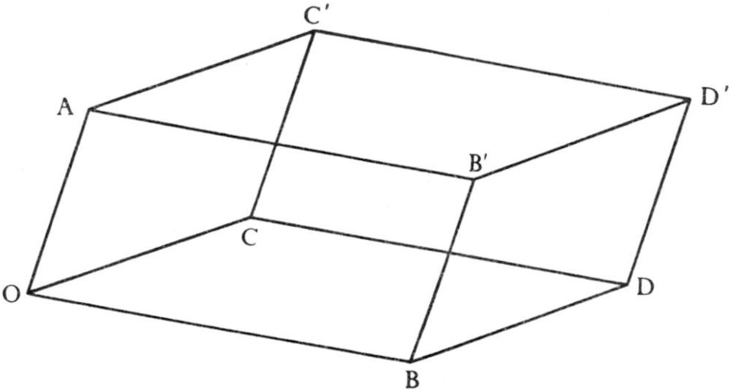

FIG. 22 The parallelepiped.

parallel to it is then called the *height*. Thus if the face OBDC is chosen as base the perpendicular distance between the plane OBDC and the plane AB′C′D′ is the height. By arguments analogous to the plane case, it can be shown that the volume of the parallelepiped is equal to the area of the base multiplied by the height. We shall now try to express the volume in terms of the vectors $\overrightarrow{OA} = \mathbf{a}$, $\overrightarrow{OB} = \mathbf{b}$, $\overrightarrow{OC} = \mathbf{c}$. Let P be the foot of the perpendicular from O on the plane AB′C′D′ and let θ be the angle POA (Fig. 23). The area of the base is $|\,\mathbf{b}\times\mathbf{c}\,|$ and the height is $|\,\mathbf{a}\,|\cos\theta$. Hence the volume V is

$$V = |\,\mathbf{a}\,|\,|\,\mathbf{b}\times\mathbf{c}\,|\cos\theta. \quad (14)$$

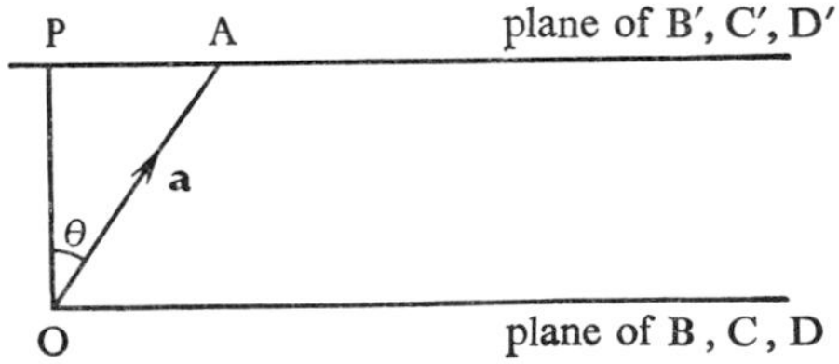

FIG. 23

Now the vector $\overrightarrow{OP}$ has the same direction as $\mathbf{b}\times\mathbf{c}$ and it has the same sense if **a, b, c** is a right-handed system. Thus, if **a, b, c** is right-handed, θ is also the angle between **a** and $\mathbf{b}\times\mathbf{c}$, and the formula above for V can be expressed as a scalar product

$$V = \mathbf{a}.(\mathbf{b}\times\mathbf{c}).$$

If, on the other hand, **a, b, c** is a left-handed system, OP will have the direction and sense of $-\mathbf{b}\times\mathbf{c}$, and then we have

$$V = -\mathbf{a}.(\mathbf{b}\times\mathbf{c}).$$

Of course the volume is independent of the order in which the vectors are taken, and bearing in mind the effect of re-ordering on left- and right-handed systems (§ 2), we have the identities

$$\begin{aligned}\mathbf{a}.(\mathbf{b}\times\mathbf{c}) = \mathbf{b}.(\mathbf{c}\times\mathbf{a}) = \mathbf{c}.(\mathbf{a}\times\mathbf{b}) = \\ -\mathbf{a}.(\mathbf{c}\times\mathbf{b}) = -\mathbf{b}.(\mathbf{a}\times\mathbf{c}) = -\mathbf{c}.(\mathbf{b}\times\mathbf{a}).\end{aligned} \tag{15}$$

Therefore, in the expression $\mathbf{a}.(\mathbf{b}\times\mathbf{c})$, it does not matter if the position of the dot and cross are interchanged. For this reason the expression is often written [**a, b, c**] and called the *scalar triple product*.

From the component formulae for scalar and vector products, we have

$$\mathbf{a}.(\mathbf{b}\times\mathbf{c}) = \sum a_1(b_2c_3-b_3c_2),$$

the sum being taken over cyclic interchanges of the suffixes 1, 2 and 3. Some students may recognize this as a determinant

$$\begin{vmatrix} a_1 & a_2 & a_3 \\ b_1 & b_2 & b_3 \\ c_1 & c_2 & c_3 \end{vmatrix}$$

the rules (15) above corresponding to the rules giving the effect of interchanging rows in a determinant.

12. The use of cross-multiplication in elimination problems

We end this chapter by a digression indicating how the algebra of § 9 is often useful in elimination problems. We saw in § 9 that, if $\mathbf{a}.\mathbf{x} = \mathbf{b}.\mathbf{x} = 0$, then $\mathbf{x}$ is of the form $k(\mathbf{a}\times\mathbf{b})$, where k is a number, provided only that $\mathbf{a}\times\mathbf{b}$ does not vanish.

Algebraically, this means that the equations

$$\begin{aligned} ax+by+cz &= 0, \\ a'x+b'y+c'z &= 0 \end{aligned}$$

imply

$$x = k(bc'-b'c), \quad y = k(ca'-c'a), \quad z = k(ab'-a'b),$$

where k is some number. This is valid only if at least one of the expressions in brackets does not vanish. We give three examples to illustrate the use of this fact.

Example 1. Eliminate θ between the equations

$$a \cos \theta + b \sin \theta + c = 0,$$
$$a' \cos \theta + b' \sin \theta + c' = 0.$$

Solution. If we apply the above formula with $x = \cos \theta$, $y = \sin \theta$, $z = 1$, we find

$$\cos \theta = k(bc' - b'c), \quad \sin \theta = k(ca' - c'a), \quad 1 = k(ab' - a'b).$$

We neglect for the moment the possibility that all the expressions in brackets should vanish. Since $\cos^2 \theta + \sin^2 \theta = 1$, we find, on squaring and adding the equations and dividing by k^2,

$$(bc' - b'c)^2 + (ca' - c'a)^2 = (ab' - a'b)^2. \tag{16}$$

If the expressions in brackets should vanish, this is still true, so (16) is the desired relation.

Example 2. Eliminate x', y' between the equations

$$\frac{xx'}{a^2} + \frac{yy'}{b^2} = 1, \quad \frac{x'^2}{a^2} + \frac{y'^2}{b^2} = 1, \quad \frac{px'}{a^2} + \frac{qy'}{b^2} = 1.$$

(*Note.* These equations express the fact that there is a point (x', y') on the ellipse with standard equation such that (x, y) and (p, q) both lie on the tangent to the ellipse at this point. Thus the result of the elimination is the equation of the pair of tangents to the ellipse from (p, q).)

Solution. We may simplify by writing $u = x'/a^2$, $v = y'/b^2$, so that the equations take the form

$$ux + vy = 1, \quad up + vq = 1, \quad a^2u^2 + b^2v^2 = 1.$$

From the first two equations we derive, by 'cross-multiplication',

$$\frac{y - q}{u} = \frac{p - x}{v} = \frac{qx - py}{-1}.$$

Combining this with the last equation, we derive

$$a^2(y - q)^2 + b^2(p - x)^2 = (qx - py)^2.$$

Example 3. Solve the equations, where a, b, c are unequal:

$$x+y+z = 0,$$
$$ax+by+cz = 0,$$
$$a^2x+b^2y+c^2z+xyz = 0.$$

Solution. From the first two equations, as before, we derive

$$x = k(b-c), \quad y = k(c-a), \quad z = k(a-b).$$

Substitute in the third equation:

$$k\sum a^2(b-c)+k^3(b-c)(c-a)(a-b) = 0.$$

Now $$\sum a^2(b-c) = -(b-c)(c-a)(a-b).$$

Hence $k^3 = k$, and $k = 0, 1,$ or -1.

There are three solutions:

(i) $x = y = z = 0,$

(ii) $x = b-c, \quad y = c-a, \quad z = a-b,$

(iii) $x = c-b, \quad y = a-c, \quad z = b-a.$

Exercises on Chapter 5

1. Prove from the definitions that

$$|\mathbf{a}\times\mathbf{b}|^2 = |\mathbf{a}|^2|\mathbf{b}|^2-(\mathbf{a}.\mathbf{b})^2.$$

2. If the vertices of a triangle have position vectors **a, b, c,** show that the area of the triangle is half the magnitude of the vector

$$\mathbf{b}\times\mathbf{c}+\mathbf{c}\times\mathbf{a}+\mathbf{a}\times\mathbf{b}.$$

Deduce that the three points lie on a line if

$$\mathbf{b}\times\mathbf{c}+\mathbf{c}\times\mathbf{a}+\mathbf{a}\times\mathbf{b} = \mathbf{0}.$$

3. Show that

$$(r\mathbf{a}+s\mathbf{b})\times(t\mathbf{a}+u\mathbf{b}) = (ru-st)(\mathbf{a}\times\mathbf{b}).$$

4. (a) Let **n** be any unit vector, and let P denote a plane perpendicular to **n.** Show that the projection of **x** on P is

$$\mathbf{x}-(\mathbf{x}.\mathbf{n})\mathbf{n}.$$

(b) A rigid body is rotated through an angle of 90 degrees in a right-handed sense about an axis passing through the origin. The unit vector giving the direction and sense of the axis of rotation is **n.** If the position vector of a point of the body before rotation is **x,** show that its position vector after rotation is

$$\mathbf{n}\times\mathbf{x}+(\mathbf{x}.\mathbf{n})\mathbf{n}.$$

5. If $\mathbf{a} \neq \mathbf{0}$ and $\mathbf{a}.\mathbf{b} = \mathbf{0}$, show that the set of points whose position vectors $\mathbf{x}$ satisfy the equation

$$\mathbf{a}\times\mathbf{x} = \mathbf{b}$$

is a straight line.

6. Let $\mathbf{a} = (3, 2, -1)$, $\mathbf{b} = (1, -1, -2)$, $\mathbf{c} = (4, -3, 4)$. Evaluate the following expressions, giving the three components if the answer is a vector.

(i) $\mathbf{a}\times(\mathbf{b}\times\mathbf{c})$, (ii) $(\mathbf{a}\times\mathbf{b})\times\mathbf{c}$, (iii) $(\mathbf{a}\times\mathbf{b}).(\mathbf{a}\times\mathbf{c})$,
(iv) $(\mathbf{a}\times\mathbf{b}).(\mathbf{b}\times\mathbf{c})$, (v) $[\mathbf{a}\times(\mathbf{a}\times\mathbf{b})].\mathbf{c}$.

7. If $\mathbf{a} = (3, 1, 2)$, $\mathbf{b} = (0, 2, -1)$, $\mathbf{c} = (1, 1, 1)$ and $\mathbf{d} = \mathbf{b}\times(\mathbf{c}\times\mathbf{a}) + (\mathbf{a}.\mathbf{c})\mathbf{a}$, show that $\mathbf{b}$ is perpendicular to $\mathbf{d}$.

8. Let $\mathbf{v}$ be a unit vector and $\mathbf{a}$ a vector such that $\mathbf{a}.\mathbf{v} = 0$. Show, directly from the definition, that, if $\mathbf{b} = \mathbf{v}\times\mathbf{a}$, then $\mathbf{v}\times\mathbf{b} = -\mathbf{a}$. Verify this when $\mathbf{a} = (2, -2, 1)$, $\mathbf{v} = (\frac{1}{3}, \frac{2}{3}, \frac{2}{3})$.

9. Let $\mathbf{a}, \mathbf{b}, \mathbf{c}$ be non-zero vectors. If $\mathbf{a}\times\mathbf{b} = \mathbf{c}$ and $\mathbf{b}\times\mathbf{c} = \mathbf{a}$, show that $\mathbf{a}, \mathbf{b}, \mathbf{c}$ are mutually perpendicular, that two of $\mathbf{a}, \mathbf{b}, \mathbf{c}$ are of equal magnitude and that the third is a unit vector. Under what condition does $\mathbf{c}\times\mathbf{a} = \mathbf{b}$ also hold in addition to the above relations?

10. Suppose that $\mathbf{a}, \mathbf{b}, \mathbf{c}$ are distinct unit vectors such that $\mathbf{a}\times\mathbf{c} = \mathbf{b}\times\mathbf{c}$ and the angle between $\mathbf{a}$ and $\mathbf{c}$ is 45°. Show that $\mathbf{a}$ is at right angles to $\mathbf{b}$.

11. **(a)** The direction and sense of an axis L through the origin is given by a unit vector $\mathbf{v}$. If a rotation through an angle θ in the right-handed sense is carried out, show that the displaced position of a point which originally had position vector $\mathbf{x}$, is given by the expression

$$(1-\cos\theta)(\mathbf{x}.\mathbf{v})\mathbf{v}+\cos\theta\,\mathbf{x}+\sin\theta(\mathbf{v}\times\mathbf{x}).$$

(b) What is the displaced position, after rotation through an angle 45° about the axis given by the vector (2, 2, 1) of the point whose original position was (1, 1, 1)?

12. If $\mathbf{c} = p\mathbf{a}+q\mathbf{b}+r(\mathbf{a}\times\mathbf{b})$, where $\mathbf{a}$ and $\mathbf{b}$ are unit vectors at an angle of 60°, show that

$$|\,\mathbf{c}\,|^2 = p^2+q^2+pq+\tfrac{3}{4}r^2.$$

Obtain similar expressions for $\mathbf{c}.\mathbf{a}$, $\mathbf{c}.\mathbf{b}$. What values must p, q, r have if $\mathbf{c}$ is a unit vector making an angle of 60° with $\mathbf{a}$ and at right angles to $\mathbf{b}$?

6

COORDINATE GEOMETRY OF THE PLANE AND STRAIGHT LINE

1. Introduction

This chapter deals with the simplest loci, the plane and the straight line, and their definition by means of equations. A straight line requires two equations to define it, a plane only one. Before considering the details, one must be quite sure what is meant by the phrases 'the equation(s) of a locus' and 'the locus defined by an equation'. This is explained in § 2 and in §§ 8 to 10. As one might expect from plane geometry, the plane and straight line in space are defined by equations of the first degree.

The algebra of vectors is helpful in deriving the equations of these loci, and even more helpful in giving a geometrical meaning to certain constants in the equations. Two sets of constants are particularly concerned, the *direction ratios* of a line and the *direction ratios* of a plane. Each of these sets of constants is the set of components of a vector, in the first case a vector parallel to the given line and in the second case a vector perpendicular (or normal) to the given plane. The numbers have significance only through the vector of which they are components—it is the vector that counts. Though there is always a risk in altering established terminology, it seems that this is a clear case for change, and we have introduced the terms *direction vector* and *normal vector*. This makes discussions clearer and helps to keep the geometry of any situation before us. One would like to think that this terminology may in time gain acceptance and that the term 'direction ratio' may fall into disuse. At present, however, there are many excellent textbooks in which the standard terminology is used, and the reader will have to be familiar with both. It will help the reader to understand the relation between vector algebra and coordinate geometry if he looks through an older textbook, such as Salmon's *Analytical Geometry of Three Dimensions*, trying to re-write the equations in vector form. He will also see that the introduction of the equation is made much easier by the use of vector notation and terminology.

2. Locus defined by a single explicit equation

Hitherto we have used a notation (x_1, x_2, x_3) for the components of a vector $\mathbf{x}$, and also for the coordinates of a typical point. In this chapter we shall most often use the letters (x, y, z) for the coordinates of a typical point, though it will occasionally be convenient to use the earlier notation still.

Consider the 'equation'

$$x^2+y^2+z^2 = 1. \tag{1}$$

If we substitute three numerical values for x, y, z in (1) the resulting statement may be true or false. If it is true, we say that the numerical values *satisfy* the equation. Thus the values $x = \frac{1}{3}$, $y = z = \frac{2}{3}$, satisfy the equation, but the values $x = 1$, $y = 2$, $z = 3$ do not.

Now consider some fixed coordinate system in space. Each point of space has three coordinates in the system. The points whose coordinates satisfy the equation are said to form *the locus defined by the equation.* The equation (1) itself, for instance, defines a sphere of unit radius, centre at the origin, because $x^2+y^2+z^2$ is the distance from the origin of the point (x, y, z).

The statement that an equation defines a given locus is really a combination of two statements:

(i) if a point lies on the locus, then its coordinates satisfy the equation;

(ii) if the coordinates of a point satisfy the equation, then the point lies on the locus.

The phrase 'if and only if' is often used in mathematics to combine two statements related in this way:

'A point lies on the locus *if and only if* its coordinates satisfy the equation.'

There are two other ways of expressing the relationship defined by the phrase 'if and only if'. One can use the phrase 'necessary and sufficient condition', thus:

'*A necessary and sufficient condition* for a point to lie on the locus is that its coordinates should satisfy the equation.' The third way is to use the term 'equivalent'. Two statements are called equivalent if each implies the other, thus:

'The following two statements are *equivalent*:

(i) the point P lies on the locus L;
(ii) the coordinates of P satisfy the equation of L.'

For shortness we shall sometimes use expressions such as 'the locus $x^2+y^2+z^2 = 1$' to mean 'the locus defined by the equation $x^2+y^2+z^2 = 1$'. Similarly we shall often say that 'the point P satisfies the equation', meaning, strictly, that 'the coordinates of the point P satisfy the equation'.

It should be noted, finally, that the locus defined by a given equation depends on the choice of coordinate system. A change of coordinate system may, and usually will, assign a different locus to the equation.

3. Basic assumptions about the plane. Normal vector

In obtaining the equation of the plane, as elsewhere in this book, we assume that the space with which we are dealing has the intuitively obvious properties of the space in which we live. In most cases we make these assumptions without stating specifically what they are, but to fix ideas we now state explicitly the assumptions that we need to obtain the equation of a plane.

We assume that, given any plane, there is a unique direction, said to be *perpendicular* to the plane, which is at right angles to the direction of *any vector* which lies in the plane. Any vector with direction perpendicular to the plane is called a *normal vector* of the plane. Given a point P and a non-zero vector **a**, we assume that there is a unique plane Π containing P with normal vector **a**. Finally, we assume that if Π is a plane, P a fixed point in Π, and **a** a normal vector of Π, then a point X lies in Π if and only if $\overrightarrow{PX}$ is at right angles to **a**.

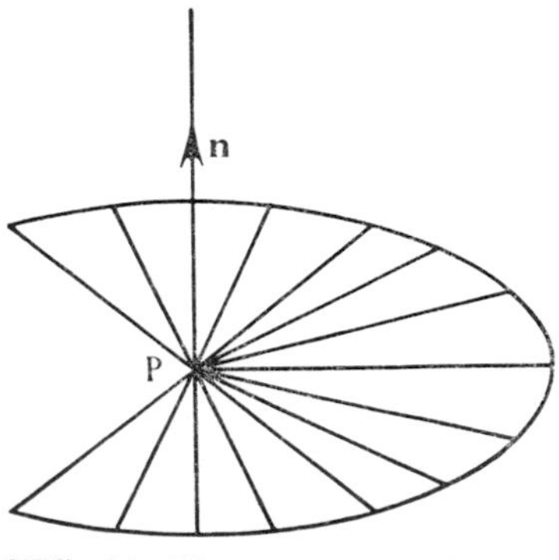

FIG. 24 Plane swept out by the family of lines through a given point P perpendicular to a normal vector **n**.

Only the direction of a vector is taken into account in deciding whether it is normal to a given plane. Thus if **a** is a normal vector of a certain plane, so is the vector $k\mathbf{a}$, $k \neq 0$, which has the same direction as **a**. On the other hand, the zero vector **0**, for which no direction is defined, cannot be a normal vector.

4. Equation of the plane

Let $\mathbf{a} \neq \mathbf{0}$ be a fixed vector, P(**p**) a fixed point, X(**x**) a variable point. Let Π denote the plane through P normal to **a**. Then, the following statements are equivalent.

(i) X lies on Π.

(ii) **a** is perpendicular to PX.

(iii) $\mathbf{a}.(\mathbf{x}-\mathbf{p}) = 0$.

(iv) $\mathbf{a}.\mathbf{x} = \mathbf{a}.\mathbf{p}$.

Equation (iv) is true if and only if X lies on Π. In other words, equation (iv) is the equation of Π. Writing k for the constant $\mathbf{a}.\mathbf{p}$, we find:

The equation of a plane can be written in the form

$$\mathbf{a}.\mathbf{x} = k, \tag{2}$$

where k is a constant and **a** *is a normal vector of the plane.* In terms of coordinates (x_1, x_2, x_3), the equation of a plane may be written with the aid of the formula for scalar products:

$$a_1x_1+a_2x_2+a_3x_3 = k. \tag{3}$$

If we adopt the notation (x, y, z) for coordinates, the equation of a plane is

$$ax+by+cz = k. \tag{4}$$

Thus the equation of a plane is linear in the coordinates x, y, z. We shall now show conversely that any linear equation represents a plane. As above, such an equation can always be written in the vector form $\mathbf{a}.\mathbf{x} = k$, where **a** is a vector different from zero. Let **p** be any point on this locus (for instance $\mathbf{p} = k\mathbf{a}/|\mathbf{a}|^2$). Since **p** is on the locus, $\mathbf{a}.\mathbf{p} = k$, so the equation can be written $\mathbf{a}.\mathbf{x} = \mathbf{a}.\mathbf{p}$, and it is the equation of the plane through **p** with normal vector **a**.

It is important to notice that the equation of the plane gives us its normal vector immediately, its components being the coefficients on the left-hand side of the equation. In the above equations (2), (3), (4), the normal vectors are respectively, **a**, (a_1, a_2, a_3) and (a, b, c).

Note. In most textbooks, including all older ones, the term *normal vector* is not used, and the components of a normal vector are called *direction ratios* of a plane. If the normal vector is a unit vector (there is, of course, a unit vector among the normal vectors of any plane) its components are called *direction cosines* of the plane. We have explained our reasons in § 1 for not using this terminology, but it is still standard and the reader ought to be familiar with it. If he has thoroughly mastered the vector operations and the formulae for them given in the previous chapters, he should have no difficulty in passing from the one viewpoint to the other and back again when necessary. Some students have told me that the new terminology actually helps in understanding texts which are written in the standard notation.

5. Examples on the equation of the plane

In working examples involving the equation of the plane, the following three facts are so important that it is worth while to repeat them.

1. A point lies on the plane if and only if its coordinates satisfy the equation of the plane.
2. The equation of a plane is linear, and conversely a linear equation always represents a plane.
3. The vector $\mathbf{a}$ is the normal vector of the plane $\mathbf{a}.\mathbf{x} = k$.

The third fact is particularly useful. It means that if we know a normal vector we know the left-hand side of the plane's equation, and only the constant k remains to be found. If we wish to find the equation of a plane, then, one of the first questions we should ask, is: Can we find its normal vector? As an illustration, consider the problem of finding the equation of a plane which passes through three given points. The method is indicated in the following example.

Example. Find the equation of the plane containing the three points A, B, C in each of the following two cases.

(i) A(0, 1, −1), B(1, 1, 0), C(1, 2, 0).

(ii) A(1, 2, 3), B(0, 3, 2), C(3, 0, 5).

Let us begin with case (i). Consider the vectors

$$\overrightarrow{AB} = (1, 0, 1), \qquad \overrightarrow{AC} = (1, 1, 1),$$

found by subtraction. The normal vector is perpendicular to both these so it is parallel to their vector product $(-1, 0, 1)$. The left-hand side of the equation must thus be of the form $-1x+0y+1z$, and the full equation will be $-x+z = k$. To determine the constant k, consider the point A. Since A lies in the plane, its coordinates $x = 0, y = 1, z = -1$ satisfy the equation, that is $-0+(-1) = k$. Thus $k = -1$, and the equation of the plane ABC is $-x+z = -1$.

(To check correctness of working, it is useful to verify that the points B, C also lie on the plane.)

This example might lead one to think that there is always a unique plane containing three given points. However, we shall see that this is not so in case (ii). This time the vectors

$$\overrightarrow{AB} = (-1,\ 1,\ -1) \quad \text{and} \quad \overrightarrow{AC} = (2,\ -2,\ 2)$$

are parallel. Their vector product is the zero vector $\mathbf{0}$, which cannot be a normal vector, since it has no direction. This does not mean that there is no plane containing the points. The points lie on a line and there are many different planes containing them. The complete solution is left to the reader (Ex. 2 below).

Exercises

1. Which of the following sets of three points are collinear? Find the equations of the planes containing the non-collinear sets.

(i) A(3, 5, 2), B(7, 4, 1), C(4, 6, 3);

(ii) A(0, 1, 2), B(−1, 0, −1), C(6, 7, 20);

(iii) A(4, 5, 6), B(5, 4, 3), C(3, 6, 8).

2. In the worked example (ii) above, show that the distinct planes $x-z+2 = 0$, $x+y-3 = 0$ both contain the points A, B and C. Show also that any plane containing the points A, B and C has an equation of the form

$$k(x-z+2)+l(x+y-3) = 0,$$

where k and l are constants.

6. The angle between two planes

Definition 7. The angle between two planes is defined to be the angle between their normal vectors.

This may seem a strange definition, but a reference to the figure will show that it is reasonable. Fig. 25 shows the intersections PQ, PR of two planes with the plane of the paper, which is assumed to be perpendicular to their line of intersection. The normal vectors $\overrightarrow{PA}$, $\overrightarrow{PB}$ of the two planes then lie in the plane of the paper. The angle θ between the normal vectors $\overrightarrow{PA}$, $\overrightarrow{PB}$ is

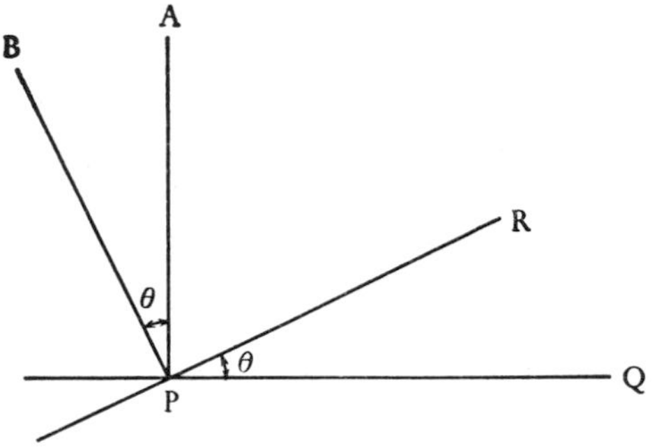

FIG. 25

equal to the angle between the lines PQ, PR and represents the amount of rotation necessary about the line of intersection to bring the plane containing PQ into coincidence with the plane containing PR. The angle θ between the planes with normal vectors **a, b** can be worked out from the formula given in Chapter 4,

$$\cos\theta = \mathbf{a}.\mathbf{b}/|\,\mathbf{a}\,|\,|\,\mathbf{b}\,|\,.$$

As an example, if the planes are $x+2y+z = 0$, and $x+y = 0$, the normal vectors are (1, 2, 1) and (1, 1, 0), with scalar product 3, so $\cos\theta = 3/\sqrt{6}.\sqrt{2} = \frac{1}{2}\sqrt{3}$, and $\theta = 30°$.

7. Perpendicular distances

Suppose given a point P(**p**) and a plane $\mathbf{a}.\mathbf{x} = k$. We wish to find a formula for the perpendicular distance of P from the plane. If Q is the foot of the perpendicular from P on the plane, then we know

(i) that Q lies on the plane, and

(ii) that PQ is parallel to the normal vector **a** (just another way of saying that PQ is perpendicular to the plane).

Express these two facts in terms of vectors, obtaining

(i) $\mathbf{a}.\mathbf{q} = k$ (Q lies on plane), (5)

(ii) $\mathbf{p}-\mathbf{q} = t\mathbf{a}$ (PQ is parallel to **a**). (6)

Take scalar products with **a** on both sides of (6). We deduce, using (5), that

$$t\,|\,\mathbf{a}\,|^2 = \mathbf{a}.\mathbf{p}-\mathbf{a}.\mathbf{q} = \mathbf{a}.\mathbf{p}-k. \tag{7}$$

Now the perpendicular distance we require is the length PQ, that is, by (6) and (7),

$$|\,\mathbf{p}-\mathbf{q}\,| = |\,t\,|\,|\,\mathbf{a}\,| = |\,\mathbf{a}.\mathbf{p}-k\,|/|\,\mathbf{a}\,|. \tag{8}$$

It will be useful later to have a formula for the perpendicular distance between two parallel planes, which will, of course, have a common normal vector **a**. Let their equations be $\mathbf{a}.\mathbf{x} = k$, $\mathbf{a}.\mathbf{x} = l$. If **p** is any point on the second plane, then $\mathbf{a}.\mathbf{p} = l$, so the perpendicular distance of **p** from the first plane is, by (8),

$$|\,\mathbf{a}.\mathbf{p}-k\,|/|\,\mathbf{a}\,| = |\,k-l\,|/|\,\mathbf{a}\,|. \tag{9}$$

The right-hand side is the expression required.

Examples. The distance of the point (1, 2, 1) from the plane $x-y+2z = 5$ is $|\,1-2+2.1-5\,|/\sqrt{(1^2+1^2+2^2)} = 4/\sqrt{6}$. (Here **a** is $(1, -1, 2)$, $k = 5$ and **p** is (1, 2, 1).) As an example of (9), the distance between the parallel planes $x+y+z = 2$ and $x+y+z = -1$ is $|\,2-(-1)\,|/\sqrt{3} = \sqrt{3}$. (Here $k = 2$, $l = -1$ and **a** is (1, 1, 1).)

8. Loci in space

In plane geometry the only kind of loci considered are lines, straight or curved, defined by a single equation. A 'locus' in the plane defined by two equations would not be of much interest; two equations in two unknowns usually only have a finite number of solutions, and such a 'locus' might consist only of a finite number of points. In space geometry, however, there are three coordinates, so two equations can be expected to define a locus which is not trivial. It is easy to convince oneself that, in general, loci defined by a single equation are *surfaces*, like the plane and the sphere, for which we have already found equations; while those defined by pairs of equations are *lines*, straight or curved. The definition of a line by means of a pair of equations (each representing a surface) is an expression of the fact that two surfaces may be expected to intersect in a line.

It is also possible to define loci by using equations involving extra variables, or *parameters*, in addition to the coordinates themselves. Both the explicit and the parametric type of equation are needed to deal with the straight line. These two methods of defining a locus are explained in detail in the next two sections.

9. Loci defined by two explicit equations

Consider the two simultaneous equations

$$x = 0, \qquad x^2+y^2+z^2 = 1. \tag{10}$$

Three numerical values for x, y and z may satisfy both equations, or one and not the other, or neither. The points whose coordinates *satisfy both equations* are said to form the *locus defined by the equations*. Thus the point $(0, \frac{3}{5}, \frac{4}{5})$ is on the locus, but the point $(\frac{1}{3}, \frac{2}{3}, \frac{2}{3})$, which satisfies only the second equation, and the point

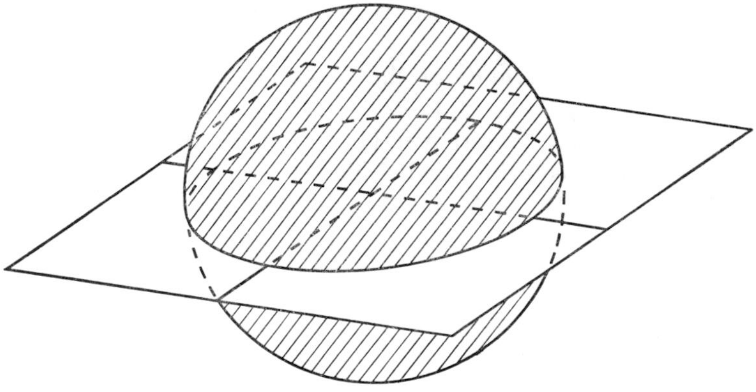

FIG. 26 Circles as the intersection of a sphere with a plane through its centre.

(3, 2, 1), which satisfies neither, are not on the locus. As in § 2, we can say: 'A point lies on the locus if and only if it satisfies both equations.' The special equations (10) define a circle, because the points which satisfy both equations lie in the plane $x = 0$ (first equation) and are at unit distance from the origin (second equation). Thus they form a circle in the plane $x = 0$ with unit radius and centre at the origin. The first equation by itself defines a plane, the second by itself represents a sphere, and the two equations combined define the intersection of the sphere with the plane through its centre, giving an example of two surfaces intersecting in a curved line (Fig. 26).

10. Parametric equations of a curve

Consider the equations

$$x = t+t^2, \quad y = t^2, \quad z = t^3. \tag{11}$$

If t is given a numerical value, the numerical values of x, y, and z are determined, and define a point of space. If t is given a different value, we obtain another point, and by allowing t to take all possible real values, we obtain a whole family of points in space called the *locus defined by the equations* (11). Equations of this type, involving one or more extra variables besides the coordinates, are called *parametric equations*. Any extra variable, such as t in equations (11), is called a *parameter*.

The letter t is very often used for the parameter, the historical reason being that such equations first arose in connexion with the path of a moving particle, equations such as (11) giving the coordinates of the point of space occupied by the particle at *time t*. It is a great help to intuition to think of parametric equations in this way.

Though parametric equations have many uses, they do not give a direct criterion whether a point does or does not lie on the locus. If we want to know this we have to consider whether there is any value of t which will, on substitution, give the coordinates of the point. For example, to find out whether the point $(-\frac{1}{4}, \frac{1}{4}, \frac{1}{8})$ lies on the locus, we have to decide whether there is a numerical value of t such that

$$t^2+t = -\tfrac{1}{4}, \quad t^2 = \tfrac{1}{4}, \quad t^3 = \tfrac{1}{8}.$$

Now the first equation is satisfied by $t = -\frac{1}{2}$ only, the second by $t = \pm\frac{1}{2}$, and the third by $t = +\frac{1}{2}$ only. Thus there is no value of t which satisfies all three and the given point does not lie on the locus. On the other hand, the point $(-\frac{1}{4}, \frac{1}{4}, -\frac{1}{8})$ corresponds to the value $t = -\frac{1}{2}$ and so does lie on the locus.

If a locus has been given parametrically and you wish to change to an explicit definition without parameters, it is often possible to do this simply by eliminating the parameters using the methods of ordinary algebra. Thus we could eliminate t from the equations

(11) in two ways to obtain the equations

$$y = (x-y)^2, \qquad z = y(x-y),$$

which are indeed a pair of explicit equations for the locus defined parametrically by (11).

However, the method of elimination should be used cautiously, because there is a danger of introducing extra loci in this way. For example, if we obtain two equations from (11) by eliminating t between the x and y equations and then by eliminating t between the y and z equations, we derive

$$y = (x-y)^2, \qquad z^2 = y^3.$$

The locus defined by these two equations does, of course, contain the curve (11), because the method of obtaining it shows that every point given by (11) must satisfy it; but it contains other points too, because the point $(-\frac{1}{4}, \frac{1}{4}, \frac{1}{8})$ lies on it though it does not, as we saw above, lie on the curve (11).

11. Direction vector of a line

The crucial step in obtaining the equation of the plane was defining a direction associated with it. Similarly to obtain equations of a line, we consider the direction of the line itself and any vector with this direction is called a *direction vector* of the line. If **a** is a direction vector, and P is a fixed point on the line, we assume that a point X lies on the line if and only if $\overrightarrow{PX}$ is parallel to **a**. Similarly we assume that, given a point P and a non-zero vector **a**, there is a unique line through P with direction vector **a**.

Everything that was said about the normal vector of a plane applies, with suitable modifications, to the direction vector of a line. Thus if **a** is a direction vector, so is $k\mathbf{a}$ if $k \neq 0$, and the zero vector cannot be a direction vector.

In many textbooks, the components of a direction vector of a line are called *direction ratios* of the line, or, if it is a unit vector, they are called its *direction cosines*. In addition to the reasons already given for modifying this terminology, it does not seem satisfactory to use the same terms in referring to planes and lines, when the relationship is so different. The direction cosines of a line (or a plane for that matter) are not completely unique. There are two unit vectors with any given direction, having opposite senses, so there is a choice of sign; but one cannot change the sign of one direction cosine without changing the sign of all three. Continual use of direction cosines (or, in our terminology, unit direction vectors) seems to lead to unnecessary introduction of irrational square roots, and we have found it better to use direction vectors of any length although they are not unique.

12. Parametric equations of a line

Let $\mathbf{a} \neq \mathbf{0}$ be a fixed vector, $P(\mathbf{p})$ a fixed point, $X(\mathbf{x})$ a variable point. We wish to find an equation for the line L which passes through P and has direction vector $\mathbf{a}$. The following four statements are equivalent.

(i) X lies on L;

(ii) $\overrightarrow{PX}$ is parallel to $\mathbf{a}$ (or is zero);

(iii) $\mathbf{x}-\mathbf{p} = t\mathbf{a}$, where t is a number (Chapter 2, § 11);

(iv) $\mathbf{x} = \mathbf{p}+t\mathbf{a}$, for some number t. (12)

Equation (iv) is thus a parametric equation of the line L, the parameter t being allowed to take all real values including the value zero. The value $t = 0$ corresponds to the point P itself.

In terms of coordinates (x_1, x_2, x_3), this single vector equation splits into three component equations

$$\left.\begin{aligned} x_1 &= p_1+ta_1, \\ x_2 &= p_2+ta_2, \\ x_3 &= p_3+ta_3, \end{aligned}\right\} \tag{13}$$

Here (p_1, p_2, p_3) is a point on L and (a_1, a_2, a_3) are the components of its direction vector.

If the (x, y, z) notation is used for coordinates, the parametric equations of the line through (p, q, r) with direction vector (a, b, c) are

$$\left.\begin{aligned} x &= p+ta, \\ y &= q+tb, \\ z &= r+tc. \end{aligned}\right\} \tag{14}$$

If none of the components of the direction vector is zero, one can eliminate the parameter t to obtain the following explicit forms instead of (13), (14) respectively:

$$\frac{x_1-p_1}{a_1} = \frac{x_2-p_2}{a_2} = \frac{x_3-p_3}{a_3}, \tag{15}$$

$$\frac{x-p}{a} = \frac{y-q}{b} = \frac{z-r}{c}. \tag{16}$$

If any of the direction ratios is zero, each of the last two forms of equation (15), (16), interpreted in the ordinary way, is meaningless, since division by zero is impossible. However, it is then possible to attach a meaning to these equations by using the convention indicated in Chapter 2, § 8, Ex. 3, that 0/0 can take any value, and a denominator can be zero provided the numerator is also. When in doubt, one should always return to the parametric form of equation.

Example. Find equations of the line joining the points A(1, 0, 2) and B(2, 1, 0).

The direction of the line is given by $\overrightarrow{AB} = (1, 1, -2)$, and A(1, 0, 2) is a point on the line. Using formula (16), with $(a, b, c) = (1, 1, -2)$ and $(p, q, r) = (1, 0, 2)$, the equations are

$$\frac{x-1}{1} = \frac{y}{1} = \frac{z-2}{-2},$$

or, in parametric form,

$$x = 1+t, \quad y = t, \quad z = 2-2t.$$

13. Non-uniqueness of the equations

The equations (15), (16) of § 12 are often referred to as the *standard form* of the equations of a line. Yet, even if we are restricted to this form, the equations of a given line are by no means unique. For instance it can easily be verified that the lines

$$\frac{x-1}{2} = \frac{y+2}{4} = \frac{z+4}{6}; \qquad \frac{x-2}{1} = \frac{y}{2} = \frac{z+1}{3}$$

are both the same, the first equations being obtained from the second simply by adding the constant 1 to all three expressions and then dividing across by 2.

It is easy to find out whether or not two lines are distinct if we are given their equations in standard form. First we check whether their direction vectors are parallel, then we take a point on one of them and check whether it lies on the other. If the vectors are parallel and if also the lines have a point in common, then the lines are the same, but if *either* of these two conditions is not satisfied, the lines are distinct.

14. Line as the intersection of two planes

When the equations of a line are written in the form (16) it is seen that the line consists of the points whose coordinates satisfy two linear equations. Each linear equation taken separately represents a plane, so the points of the line are the points common to the two planes, or, the line is the *intersection of the two planes.* Of course the linear equations (16) are of a rather special form, one involving x, y only, the other involving y, z only. It is intuitively clear, however, that the intersection of *any* two planes is a line. We shall now give an algebraic proof of this fact, though some readers may be willing to take this as a basic assumption and omit the proof.

Let $\mathbf{a}.\mathbf{x} = k$, $\mathbf{b}.\mathbf{x} = l$ be the equations of two planes which are not parallel, so that the vector $\mathbf{b}$ is not parallel to $\mathbf{a}$. Thus if θ is the angle between $\mathbf{a}$ and $\mathbf{b}$, $\cos\theta \neq 1$ and $|\mathbf{a}|^2|\mathbf{b}|^2-(\mathbf{a}.\mathbf{b})^2 \neq 0$. We show first:

There is a point $\mathbf{p}$ *which lies on both planes.*

Let $\mathbf{p} = \lambda\mathbf{a}+\mu\mathbf{b}$. We shall try to determine values of λ, μ which make $\mathbf{p}$ lie on both planes. The conditions for this are

$$\mathbf{a}.(\lambda\mathbf{a}+\mu\mathbf{b}) = k, \qquad \mathbf{b}.(\lambda\mathbf{a}+\mu\mathbf{b}) = l.$$

If we solve these simultaneous equations in λ, μ in the usual way by elimination, we find

$$\lambda\,(|\mathbf{a}|^2|\mathbf{b}|^2-(\mathbf{a}.\mathbf{b})^2) = k|\mathbf{b}|^2-l(\mathbf{a}.\mathbf{b}),$$
$$\mu\,(|\mathbf{a}|^2|\mathbf{b}|^2-(\mathbf{a}.\mathbf{b})^2) = l|\mathbf{a}|^2-k(\mathbf{a}.\mathbf{b}).$$

The common coefficient of λ, μ is not zero, so there is a solution and thus we obtain a point $\mathbf{p}$ common to the two planes.

It is now easy to show that the intersection is a line. If a point $\mathbf{x}$ lies on both planes we have $\mathbf{a}.(\mathbf{x}-\mathbf{p}) = \mathbf{b}.(\mathbf{x}-\mathbf{p}) = 0$. The vector $\mathbf{x}-\mathbf{p}$ is perpendicular to both $\mathbf{a}$ and $\mathbf{b}$, so it is parallel to their vector product. The locus of $\mathbf{x}$ is thus the line through $\mathbf{p}$ with direction vector $\mathbf{a}\times\mathbf{b}$.

The idea behind this proof may be clearer if the following numerical example is studied.

Example. Express in standard form the equations of the line of intersection of the planes:

$$x-2y+3z = 1,$$
$$2x+y+z = 3.$$

In order to obtain the equations of the line in standard form, we require two things: (i) a point on the line, (ii) a direction vector.

(i) We put $z = 0$ in the above equations, so that they reduce to two equations in two unknowns. Solving, we find $x = y = -1$. The point $(-1, -1, 0)$ thus lies on the line.

(ii) Since the line lies in both planes, its direction is perpendicular to the normal vectors of both planes. Thus the vector product of the normal vectors is a direction vector for the line of intersection. The normal vectors of the two planes are, respectively $(1, -2, 3)$ and $(2, 1, 1)$ with vector product $(-5, 5, 5)$. The equations of the line in standard form are thus

$$\frac{x+1}{-5} = \frac{y+1}{5} = \frac{z}{5},$$

or, simplified: $$-(x+1) = y+1 = z.$$

Note. It sometimes happens that, if we put $z = 0$ in the equations of the two planes, the resulting equations in x, y have no solution. In such a case it will be possible to find a point on the line by putting $x = 0$ or $y = 0$, unless, of course, the planes are parallel.

15. Angle between two lines. Angle between line and plane

There is no difficulty about defining the angle between two lines in space.

Definition 8. The angle between two lines is the angle between their direction vectors.

This is an extension of the idea of angle between two lines in plane geometry, since two lines in space do not as a rule intersect and thus do not 'contain an angle' in Euclid's sense. However, the definition is in line with the more modern concept of amount of rotation, because it is the amount of rotation necessary to bring one of the lines into a position parallel to the other. The angle between two lines can again be calculated from the formula

$$\cos\theta = \frac{\mathbf{a}.\mathbf{b}}{|\mathbf{a}||\mathbf{b}|}.$$

The problem of defining the angle between a line and a plane is not quite so straightforward. One might be tempted to define it as the angle between the direction vector of the line and the normal vector of the plane, but a moment's thought shows that this is not at all suitable. For instance, if a line actually *lies in* the plane, the angle between the line and the plane ought clearly to be zero, yet it is at right angles to the normal vector. Again, a line parallel to the normal vector ought clearly to make an angle of 90° with

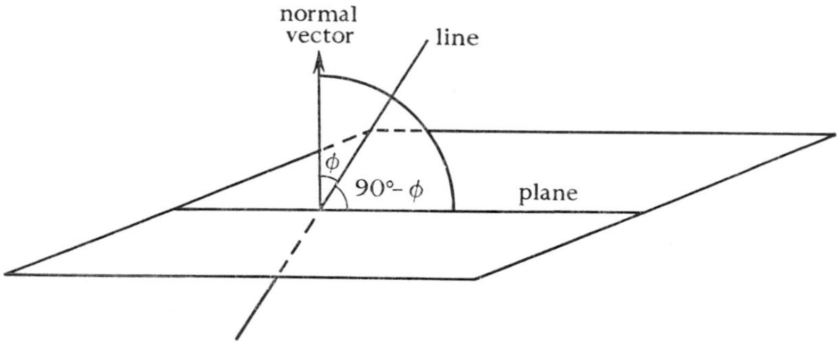

FIG. 27 Angle between line and plane.

the plane. These considerations, together with a study of Fig. 27, suggest the following definition.

Definition 9. If ϕ is the angle between the direction vector $\mathbf{a}$ of a line and the normal vector $\mathbf{b}$ of a plane, the angle θ between the line and the plane is defined to be

$$\theta = \frac{\pi}{2} - \phi.$$

The angle θ can be calculated from the formula

$$\sin\theta\ (= \cos\phi) = \frac{\mathbf{a}.\mathbf{b}}{|\mathbf{a}||\mathbf{b}|}.$$

Two other definitions of the angle between a line and a plane can be given. (i) θ is the angle between the line and its projection on the plane. (ii) θ is the minimum angle between the line and any line which lies in the plane. It is easy to verify that these definitions lead to the same value of the angle as Definition 8.

The condition that a line with direction vector **a** should be *parallel* to a plane with normal vector **b** is that the scalar product **a**.**b** should vanish, in contrast to the usual situation where vanishing scalar product is associated with perpendicularity.

Example. Find the angle between the plane $x+z = 0$ and the line of intersection of the planes $x = y$, $x+y-z = 1$.

Solution. The normal vector **a** of the first plane is (1, 0, 1). The direction vector of the line is the vector product of the normal vectors of the second and third planes:

$$(1, -1, 0)\times(1, 1, -1) = (1, 1, 2).$$

The desired angle is given by the relation

$$\sin\theta = \mathbf{a}.\mathbf{b}/|\mathbf{a}||\mathbf{b}| = 3/\sqrt{2}.\sqrt{6} = \tfrac{1}{2}\sqrt{3}.$$

Thus the angle is 60°.

Exercises 6.1

1. Find the equation of the plane containing the three points

$$(1, 0, 1),\quad (1, 1, 1),\quad (2, 1, -1)$$

2. The vertices of a triangle are (1, 0, 1), (0, 1, −1), (−2, 2, −2). Find the lengths of its sides, the cosines of its angles and its area. What is the equation of the plane containing it? Find the same information for the triangle with vertices (1, 1, −1), (2, 0, 1) and (−4, 2, 3).

3. A triangle has vertices (−1, 1, −1), (2, 3, 4), (3, 4, 6). Find its area and the perpendicular distance from the origin to the plane containing it.

4. A plane passes through the points (0, 1, 2) and (1, −1, 0). It is parallel to the direction (1, −1, 1). Find the equation of the plane and the foot of the perpendicular on it from the point (3, 0, 3).

5. For each of the following triangles, find the lengths of the sides, cosines of the angles and the coordinates of the foot of the perpendicular from the origin on the plane of the triangle.

(i) (−2, 0, 1), (−1, 1, 2), (−3, 2, 0);
(ii) (1, 1, 1), (2, 0, 1), (4, 3, 2).

6. Three points A, B, C have coordinates

$$A(1, 2, 3),\quad B(2, 3, 1),\quad C(3, 0, -1),$$

and O is the origin. Find the cosine of the angle between the planes ABC, OBC.

7. Show that the equation of the plane which cuts the coordinate axes at the points $(a, 0, 0)$, $(0, b, 0)$, $(0, 0, c)$, where a, b, and c are non-zero, is

$$\frac{x}{a}+\frac{y}{b}+\frac{z}{c} = 1.$$

Two planes cut the axes in A, B, C and A , B′, C′ respectively. If O is the origin and G, G′ are the centroids of the triangles ABC, A′B′C′ respectively, show that OG is at right angles to the plane A′B′C′ if and only if OG′ is at right angles to the plane ABC.

8. Find the point of intersection of the line with parametric equations $x = 4+t$, $y = 1-t$, $z = 3t$ and the plane $2x+4y+z = 9$.

9. Show that the intersection of the line $\mathbf{x} = \mathbf{a}+t\mathbf{b}$ (parameter t) and the plane $\mathbf{n}.\mathbf{x} = k$ has position vector

$$\mathbf{a}+\frac{k-\mathbf{n}.\mathbf{a}}{\mathbf{n}.\mathbf{b}}\mathbf{b}.$$

10. Find equations for the line through the point (3, 5, 2) perpendicular to the plane $5x-7y+4z = -2$. Obtain the coordinates of the foot of the perpendicular on the plane from the point.

11. A plane is parallel to both the lines

$$\text{(i)}\ \frac{x-1}{2} = \frac{y}{3} = \frac{z-1}{4};\qquad \text{(ii)}\ \frac{x+1}{-1} = \frac{y}{2} = \frac{z}{1}.$$

It also passes through the point (1, 0, −1). Find its equation.

12. Find the cosine of the angle between the following two lines:

(i) $x-1 = y = z-1$, (ii) $x = 1+t$, $y = 5t$, $z = -t$.

Find also the coordinates of the foot of the perpendicular from the origin on the second line.

13. Show that the three planes $y = z+1$, $z = x+1$, $x = y+1$ intersect the plane $x+y+z = 0$ in three lines which are sides of an equilateral triangle.

14. Find the direction cosines of the lines of intersection of the following three pairs of planes:

(i) $x+y+2z = 2, \quad x-y-z = 5$;
(ii) $2x-y = 3, \quad x+y+4z = 1$;
(iii) $x-y+z = 4, \quad 2x-2y-3z = 5$.

Find also equations of these three lines in parametric form, and the cosines of the angles between them.

15. Find the angle between the line $x = y$, $z = 0$ and the plane $x+z = 0$.

16. If l is the line

$$\frac{x+1}{2} = \frac{y-3}{3} = \frac{z-1}{-1},$$

and m is the line through the point (5, 4, 2) which cuts l at right angles, find equations for m and the coordinates of the point of intersection of l and m.

16. Planes containing a line of intersection

If we are given two equations, there are many ways of deriving new equations from them by the ordinary rules of algebra. Consider, for instance, the two equations of § 14,

$$x-2y+3z = 1, \qquad 2x+y+z = -3. \tag{17}$$

One could eliminate x, multiplying the first equation by 2 and subtracting the second, to obtain

$$-5y+5z = 5, \tag{18}$$

or, dividing by 5,

$$-y+z = 1. \tag{19}$$

Similarly one might eliminate y to obtain

$$x+z = -1. \tag{20}$$

Again, one could simply add the two equations together:

$$3x-y+4z = -2. \tag{21}$$

The equations (18), (19), (20), (21) are all derived from equations (17) by the same kind of process; each of the two equations (17) is multiplied by a constant and the resulting equations are added. Thus, if equations (17) are denoted by U, V, equation (18) is $2U-V$, (19) is $\frac{2}{5}U-\frac{1}{5}V$, (20) is $\frac{1}{5}U+\frac{2}{5}V$ and (21) is $U+V$. All these are included as particular cases of the general formula

$kU+lV$, which, written out in full as an equation, is

$$(k+2l)x+(-2k+l)y+(3k+l)z = k-3l. \tag{22}$$

This method of deriving new equations is the same as that used in the solution of simultaneous equations. Any solution of the simultaneous equations (17) must satisfy also the equations (18), (19), (20), (21) or, more generally (22).

What we have done so far is pure algebra, and no reference has been made to any coordinate system or to any loci in space; but of course every one of the equations we have written down does, in fact, define a locus. Since the equations are all of the first degree, they represent planes. Let us now consider the geometrical interpretation of these equations.

Any solution of the simultaneous equations (17) gives the coordinates of a point on the line L of intersection of the two planes

$$x-2y+3z = 1, \qquad 2x+y+z = -3.$$

Thus any point of L satisfies (18); in other words, equation (18) defines a locus which *contains the line* L. Also the locus (18) has a linear equation, so it is a plane. The equation (18), therefore, defines a *plane containing the line* L. The same argument shows that the other equations (19), (20), (21), (22) also define planes containing L.

Equation (22) is a general type which includes the others; for instance (18) is obtained from (22) by putting $k = 2$, $l = -1$ and (21) is obtained by putting $k = l = 1$. We shall see in the next section that *every* plane containing L can be obtained from (22) by giving suitable values to the constants k, l. First of all we illustrate the usefulness of the method by working two examples. (These examples can, of course, be worked out without using the $kU+lV$ method, by obtaining the equations of the line L in standard form and using methods of the kind given earlier in this chapter. The reader will find that these alternatives are quite a bit longer.)

Example 1. Find the equation of the plane containing the point (1, 1, 1) and also the line L defined by equations (17).

Solution. Equation (22) represents a general plane containing L. We wish to determine the constants k, l so that the point (1, 1, 1) satisfies the equation, that is,

$$(k+2l).1+(-2k+l).1+(3k+l).1 = k-3l.$$

Simplifying this, we find $k = -7l$. A possible solution is $k = 7$, $l = -1$, giving, for the equation of the plane required,

$$5x-15y+20z = 10,$$

or, divided across by 5,

$$x-3y+4z = 2.$$

Example 2. Find the equation of the plane containing the line L defined by equations (17) which is parallel to the vector (2, 1, 0).

Solution. Again we consider equation (22), which represents a plane with normal vector

$$(k+2l,\ -2k+l,\ 3k+l) \tag{23}$$

If the vector (2, 1, 0) is parallel to the plane, then it is at right angles to its normal vector (23) and their scalar product vanishes. That is,

$$2(k+2l)+1(-2k+l)+0(3k+l) = 0.$$

This reduces to $l = 0$, and the desired plane is

$$x-2y+3z = 1,$$

the first equation (17), which does, of course, define a plane containing L.

The reader may be surprised that in these examples we arrive at *one* equation in *two* unknowns k, l. This is not really surprising, since the equation of a plane may be multiplied by a constant factor without altering the locus. Thus it is the *ratio* $k:l$ that matters. For instance, equations (18), (19) denote the same locus, though (18) arises from $k = 2$, $l = -1$ and (19) arises from $k = \frac{2}{5}$, $l = -\frac{1}{5}$.

17. Planes containing a line of intersection (theory)

Suppose given two planes

$$\mathbf{a}.\mathbf{x}-k = 0, \qquad \mathbf{b}.\mathbf{x}-l = 0 \tag{24}$$

with line of intersection L. We assume, of course, that the planes are not parallel, so that the vector $\mathbf{a}$ is not a multiple of $\mathbf{b}$. If λ, μ are two constants, not both zero, we may multiply the first equation by λ, the second by μ and add, to obtain

$$(\lambda\mathbf{a}+\mu\mathbf{b}).\mathbf{x}-(\lambda k+\mu l) = 0. \tag{25}$$

The vector $\lambda\mathbf{a}+\mu\mathbf{b}$ cannot be zero, since $\mathbf{a}$ is not a multiple of $\mathbf{b}$, so equation (25) is a linear equation and represents a plane. We now prove three facts about the plane (25).

I. *The plane* (25) *contains the line* L.

II. *If* $\mathbf{p}$ *is any point not on* L, *the constants* λ, μ *can be so chosen that equation* (25) *represents a plane passing through* $\mathbf{p}$.

III. *Every plane containing* L *has an equation of the form* (25).

Proof of I. If a vector $\mathbf{x}$ satisfies both equations (24), then it satisfies equation (25), so the position vector of any point of L satisfies (25). Thus every point of L lies on the plane (25) and the plane contains the whole of L.

Proof of II. The condition that $\mathbf{p}$ should lie on the plane (25) is simply $\lambda(\mathbf{a}.\mathbf{p}-k)+\mu(\mathbf{b}.\mathbf{p}-l) = 0$. This is certainly true when λ, μ take the special values $\lambda = \mathbf{b}.\mathbf{p}-l$, $\mu = -(\mathbf{a}.\mathbf{p}-k)$. These are not both zero, since $\mathbf{p}$ does not lie on L.

Proof of III. Let Π be any plane containing L. Let $\mathbf{p}$ be any point of Π which does not lie on L. By II, we can find a plane Π' with an equation of the form (25) which passes through $\mathbf{p}$. Then Π and Π' must coincide, for their intersection contains the point $\mathbf{p}$ as well as the line L, though the intersection (if any) of two distinct planes is a line only. Thus $\Pi = \Pi'$, and Π does indeed have an equation of the form (25).

18. Problems

The theory that has now been given includes the basic information needed to solve a fair variety of problems about planes and straight lines in space. Many different types of problem can be set, and one cannot expect to prepare in advance for all types. One must be ready to meet problems of types one has not seen before and expect to spend some time planning a sequence of steps for the solution before beginning calculations. Problems will vary from relatively simple ones, like the equation of a plane containing three given points, to quite intricate ones, such as the problem of finding the shortest distance between two non-intersecting lines, which we shall deal with in detail in § 19. With these more involved problems, it is a good idea to write down a plan on paper before beginning to calculate. First you should attach names or symbols to the points, planes, lines and vectors occurring; it is a good idea to include normal vectors and direction vectors, though these will not always be needed in the solution. Then, write down, in the form of equations if possible, any geometrical information given in the question. After that, plan your way through the question step by step. Do not be in too much of a hurry—once a plan has been made, the detailed working will require surprisingly little time. Each problem has to be considered on its merits. There is no standard method which will solve all problems, nor is there a single 'right method' of solving any particular problem. Any logically valid method is right, though some may be longer than others. We shall illustrate this point by giving more than one method of solution for some of the problems given below.

Problem 1. A plane contains the line

$$\frac{x-1}{1} = \frac{y-2}{-1} = \frac{z-1}{2},$$

and is parallel to the line

$$\frac{x}{1} = \frac{y+7}{2} = \frac{z}{3}$$

Find its equation.

First method. Call the first line L, the second M and the plane P. Let the direction vectors of L, M be $\mathbf{a}$, $\mathbf{b}$, and the normal vector of P be $\mathbf{n}$. Clearly $\mathbf{n}$ is at right angles to $\mathbf{a}$, $\mathbf{b}$ (§ 15), so we may take $\mathbf{n} = \mathbf{a}\times\mathbf{b}$. This gives the left side of the equation of P. To find the constant, we need one point on P—a point on L will do. In the actual problem as given, $\mathbf{a} = (1, -1, 2)$, $\mathbf{b} = (1, 2, 3)$, so that $\mathbf{n} = \mathbf{a}\times\mathbf{b} = (-7, -1, 3)$, giving for P an equation of the form $-7x-y+3z = k$. Now the point $(1, 2, 1)$ lies on L and therefore on P, so $k = -7.1-2+3.1 = -6$. Thus the answer is

$$-7x-y+3z = -6.$$

Second method. Use the $kU+lV$ theory (§ 16, Ex. 2). For this the line L must be defined as the intersection of two planes, which we may take to be

$$\frac{x-1}{1} = \frac{y-2}{-1} \quad \text{and} \quad \frac{y-2}{-1} = \frac{z-1}{2},$$

or, $$x+y = 3 \quad \text{and} \quad 2y+z = 5.$$

Multiply the first of these equations by k, the second by l, and add, to obtain the general plane containing L, that is:

$$kx+(k+2l)y+lz = 3k+5l.$$

The normal vector $(k, k+2l, l)$ must be at right angles to the direction (1, 2, 3) of M. Thus the scalar product of these two vectors vanishes: $k+2(k+2l)+3l = 0$. This gives $k = -7$, $l = 3$, and the equation $-7x-y+3z = -6$, as before.

Problem 2. Find the equations of the projection of the line

$$\frac{x-5}{3} = y = z-4 \tag{26}$$

on the plane $$x+2y+z = 3. \tag{27}$$

Solution. The *projection* of a line or curve on a plane, of course, is the locus of the feet of the perpendiculars from its points on the plane. This is a type of question where the parametric form of equations is clearly useful. The parametric equations give the coordinates of a 'typical point' on the locus. We can find the coordinates of the foot of the perpendicular from this typical point on the plane. This will be a typical point on the projection, and the expression for it will constitute parametric equations for the projection. To carry out this plan, let us write equations (26) in parametric form:

$$\mathrm{P}(x, y, z) = (5+3t, t, 4+t)$$

If Q is the foot of the perpendicular from P on the plane, then $\overrightarrow{\mathrm{PQ}}$ is parallel to the normal vector (1, 2, 1), that is $\overrightarrow{\mathrm{PQ}} = (k, 2k, k)$, where k is a number. Then the position vector of Q will be $\overrightarrow{\mathrm{OQ}} = \overrightarrow{\mathrm{OP}}+\overrightarrow{\mathrm{PQ}}$, or

$$(5+3t+k, t+2k, 4+t+k).$$

Now Q lies on the plane (27), so its coordinates satisfy the equation (27) and we have

$$5+3t+k+2(t+2k)+4+t+k = 3,$$

reducing to $k = -t-1$. Substituting for k, we find that Q is the point $(4+2t, \ -2-t, \ 3)$. This is the desired expression for the coordinates of a typical point on the projection, and the parametric equations for the projection are

$$x = 4+2t, \quad y = -2-t, \quad z = 3.$$

This should be an adequate answer to the question as set above, for if it is not specified whether explicit or parametric equations are required, one should assume that either will do. If we had been asked for explicit equations for the projection, however, we should now eliminate the parameter t to find

$$\frac{x-4}{2} = \frac{y+2}{-1}, \qquad z = 3.$$

Problem 3. Let O be the origin, and let L be the line with equations

$$x = \frac{y-1}{2} = z-3.$$

Find a point P on L such that OP makes an angle of 45 degrees with L.

First method. The direction of L is $\mathbf{a} = (1, 2, 1)$. If P lies on L, then, for some value of t, we have $\overrightarrow{OP} = (t, \ 1+2t, \ 3+t)$. For the angle between $\overrightarrow{OP}$ and $\mathbf{a}$ to be 45°, we must have, by the definition of scalar product,

$$\mathbf{a}.\overrightarrow{OP} = |\,\mathbf{a}\,|\,|\,\overrightarrow{OP}\,|/\sqrt{2},$$

which reduces, on using the formulae, to

$$6t+5 = \sqrt{6}\ \sqrt{(6t^2+10t+10)}/\sqrt{2}.$$

Squared and simplified, this reduces to

$$18t^2+30t-5 = 0,$$

giving $t = \frac{1}{6}(-5\pm\sqrt{35})$. The two values of t give two points P satisfying the conditions:

$$(-\tfrac{5}{6}+\tfrac{1}{6}\sqrt{35},\quad -\tfrac{2}{3}+\tfrac{1}{3}\sqrt{35},\quad \tfrac{13}{6}+\tfrac{1}{6}\sqrt{35}),$$
$$(-\tfrac{5}{6}-\tfrac{1}{6}\sqrt{35},\quad -\tfrac{2}{3}-\tfrac{1}{3}\sqrt{35},\quad \tfrac{13}{6}-\tfrac{1}{6}\sqrt{35}).$$

Second method. If X is the foot of the perpendicular from O on L, then XP must be equal in length to OX (Fig. 28). Let us begin

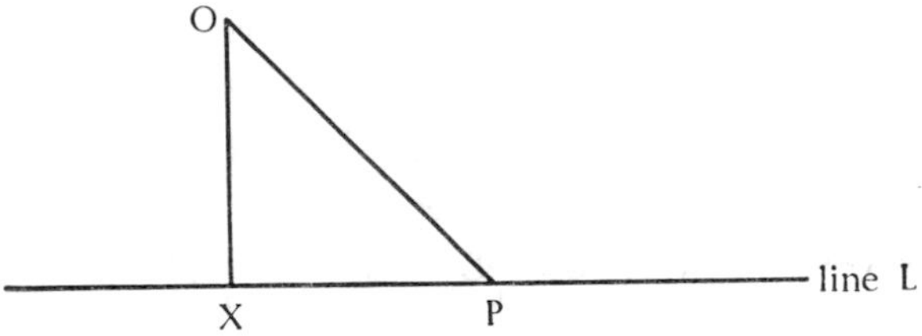

FIG. 28

by finding the coordinates of X. Since X is on the line L, we must have, for some value of t,

$$\overrightarrow{OX} = (t,\ 1+2t,\ 3+t). \tag{28}$$

We want to choose the value of t which makes $\overrightarrow{OX}$ perpendicular to L, that is, the scalar product of $\overrightarrow{OX}$ with the direction vector (1, 2, 1) of L must vanish. The condition for this is found to be $5+6t = 0$, $t = -\frac{5}{6}$. Substituting for t in (28), we find

$$\overrightarrow{OX} = (-\tfrac{5}{6},\ -\tfrac{2}{3},\ \tfrac{13}{6}) \quad \text{and} \quad |\,OX\,|^2 = \tfrac{35}{6}.$$

Now XP is parallel to (1, 2, 1), since it joins two points on L. Thus there is a value of u such that $\overrightarrow{XP} = (u, 2u, u)$. From the equation $|\,XP\,|^2 = |\,OX\,|^2$, we find that $u = \pm\frac{1}{6}\sqrt{35}$, so that

$$\overrightarrow{OP} = \overrightarrow{OX}+\overrightarrow{XP} = \tfrac{1}{6}(-5,\ -4,\ 13)\pm\tfrac{1}{6}\sqrt{35}(1,\ 2,\ 1),$$

as found before.

Problem 4. A line contains the point (1, 0, 2) and meets each of the lines

$$x = y = z+2, \tag{29}$$
$$x+3 = -\tfrac{1}{2}y = \tfrac{1}{3}z. \tag{30}$$

Find its equations.

First method. Call the known lines L, M, the unknown line N. Let (a, b, c) be a direction vector of N. Then a typical point on N will be $(1+at, bt, 2+ct)$, where t is the parameter. If the point P where L meets N corresponds to the value $t = k$ of the parameter, the coordinates $(1+ak, bk, 2+ck)$ of P must satisfy equations (29), giving

$$1+ak = bk = 4+ck. \tag{31}$$

If the point Q where M meets N corresponds to the value $t = l$ of the parameter, it follows by a similar argument that

$$4+al = -\tfrac{1}{2}bl = \tfrac{1}{3}(2+cl). \tag{32}$$

All our information has now been written down in the form of equations (31) and (32), giving only four equations in the five unknowns a, b, c, k, l. It might thus seem that we have too few equations, but again, as in § 16, we have a case where only the ratios of three of the variables matters. The variables a, b, c in fact represent a direction, and it is merely their ratio that is important. To complete the solution, eliminate k from equations (31) and l from equations (32). We find

$$4a-3b-c = 0, \qquad 2a-5b-4c = 0.$$

From these we find that $a : b : c = 1 : 2 : -2$, and the equations of the line are

$$x-1 = \frac{y}{2} = -\frac{z-2}{2}.$$

Second method. Let A denote the point (1, 0, 2). The plane through L containing A, which we shall call the plane (A, L), must contain N since it contains two points of it, the point A and the point P. Similarly, the plane (A, M) contains N; in fact, N is the intersection of the planes (A, L), (A, M). Our plan then is: Find the equations of the planes (A, L) and (A, M). These two equations together define the line N.

The plane (A, L) contains the point A(1, 0, 2) and also the point (0, 0, −2) on L. Thus its normal vector is at right angles to the vector (1, 0, 4) joining these points. Its normal vector is also at right angles to the direction vector (1, 1, 1) of L. A possible normal vector is thus the vector product (−4, 3, 1). Using the fact that the point (0, 0, −2) is on L, the equation of the plane

(A, L) is found to be

$$-4x+3y+z = -2. \tag{33}$$

An exactly similar method gives us the plane (A, M):

$$2x-5y-4z = -6. \tag{34}$$

Equations (33), (34), taken together, are a set of equations for N. If equations in standard form are required, they can be worked out as in § 14.

19. The common perpendicular of two skew lines

Two lines L, M in space each defined by two equations, represent a total of four equations in three unknowns. There is not, in general, a solution, so the two lines do not usually intersect. Two lines in space which do not intersect and are not parallel, are called *skew*. If L, M are skew lines, one may look for two points, P on L, Q on M, for which the distance PQ is as small as possible. It is easy to convince oneself that this minimum value occurs when PQ is at right angles to both lines. The length PQ is then

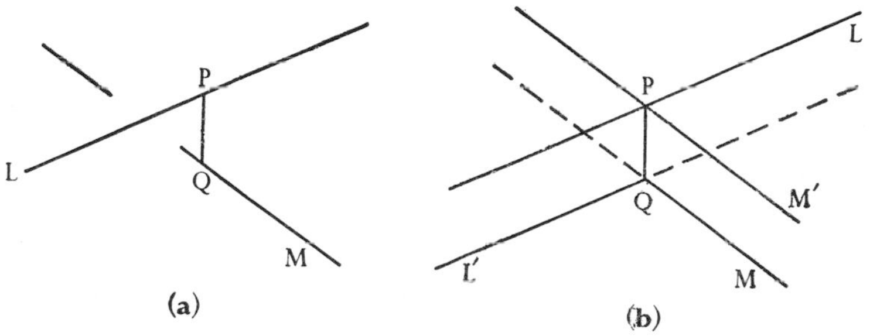

FIG. 29

called the *shortest distance* between the lines, and the line PQ is called their *common perpendicular*.

The problems of finding the points P, Q, the equations of the common perpendicular, and the shortest distance when the equations of L, M are given, can be solved in several different ways. Before considering these, let us study the diagram consisting of the two lines L, M and the points P, Q at the ends of the common perpendicular (Fig. 29a). To make the diagram more symmetrical, it seems natural to add to it the line L' through Q parallel to L and the line M' through P parallel to M (Fig. 29b). The new diagram resembles two wedges placed edge to edge. It contains five lines PQ, L, L', M, M', four planes PQLL', PQMM', LM', $L'M$ and the two points P, Q. Notice that the planes LM', $L'M$ are parallel, that PQ is a normal vector of each of them and that the shortest distance between L and M is the perpendicular distance between these parallel planes. It is now easy to see many ways of attacking the problem. We give two methods, taking the following numerical example.

Example. Find (i) the shortest distance,
(ii) the equations of the common perpendicular,
(iii) the coordinates of the feet of the common perpendicular,

for the two lines

$$L: \quad x-1 = y = z+5, \tag{35}$$

$$M: \quad \frac{x}{3} = \frac{y+2}{2} = z+2. \tag{36}$$

First method. Write down the direction vectors of L, M:

$$\mathbf{a} = (1, 1, 1), \qquad \mathbf{b} = (3, 2, 1).$$

Any point P on L has coordinates

$$(1+t,\ t,\ -5+t), \tag{37}$$

and any point Q on M has coordinates

$$(3u,\ -2+2u,\ -2+u). \tag{38}$$

We have to choose the values of the parameters t, u so as to make sure that $\overrightarrow{PQ}$ is at right angles to both $\mathbf{a}$ and $\mathbf{b}$, that is, so that the two scalar products $\overrightarrow{PQ}.\mathbf{a}$ and $\overrightarrow{PQ}.\mathbf{b}$ both vanish. By subtraction, we find that

$$\overrightarrow{PQ} = (-1-t+3u,\ -2-t+2u,\ 3-t+u).$$

Using the formula for scalar product, we find the two equations

$$\overrightarrow{PQ}.\mathbf{a} = -3t+6u = 0, \qquad \overrightarrow{PQ}.\mathbf{b} = -4-6t+14u = 0.$$

These have the solution $t = 4$, $u = 2$, so the desired points P, Q, obtained by substitution in (37), (38) are P(5, 4, -1), Q(6, 2, 0). Thus $\overrightarrow{PQ} = (1,\ -2,\ 1)$, and the shortest distance $= |\mathrm{PQ}| = \sqrt{6}$.

Equations of the line PQ, from its direction PQ and the point P on it, are:

$$x-5 = \frac{y-4}{-2} = z+1.$$

Second method. We find PQ as the intersection of the plane $PQLL'$, which we call Π_1, and the plane $PQMM'$, which we call Π_2.

Detailed plan

(i) Work out direction vector of PQ. Call this **c**.
(ii) Work out equation of Π_1.
(iii) Work out equation of Π_2.
(iv) Obtain Q as the intersection of Π_1 and M.
(v) Obtain P as the intersection of Π_2 and L.
(vi) Shortest distance $= |PQ|$.

Actual working

(i) PQ is at right angles to **a**, **b**, so $\mathbf{c} = \mathbf{a}\times\mathbf{b} = (1, -2, 1)$.

(ii) Π_1 contains PQ, parallel to **c**, and it also contains L, parallel to **a**. Normal vector of $\Pi_1 = \mathbf{c}\times\mathbf{a} = (-3, 0, 3)$. Dividing by common factor 3, Π_1 has equation $-x+z = k$. Point $(1, 0, -5)$ on L is on Π_1, so $k = -1-5 = -6$.

Equation of Π_1: $-x+z = -6$. (39)

(iii) As in (ii), one finds

Equation of Π_2: $-2x+y+4z = -10$. (40)

(iv) Q is on M, so its coordinates (x, y, z) satisfy the equations (36) of M. Also Q is on Π_1, so it satisfies equation (39). Solving equations (36) and (39) we find that Q is (6, 2, 0).

(v) A similar calculation gives P(5, 4, −1).

(vi) As before, $|PQ| = \sqrt{6}$.

Notes

(*a*) In the second method, the equations of the common perpendicular are obtained as (39) and (40) simultaneously. There is no need to go further than Step (iii) if only the equations of the common perpendicular are needed. On the other hand, if all the information is required, the first method is rather shorter.

(*b*) Neither method works out the problems in the order in

which they are posed. The first method answers the questions in the order (iii), (i), (ii) and the second method answers them in the order (ii), (iii), (i). It is a mistake to suppose that the logical order for answering a number of related questions is necessarily the order in which they are asked.

Third method (for shortest distance only)

Sometimes only the shortest distance is needed, not the actual points P, Q or the equations of PQ. In that case the following method is best.

The shortest distance is the perpendicular distance between the planes LM', $L'M$. Both these planes have normal vector $\mathbf{a}\times\mathbf{b} = (1, -2, 1)$, so their equations are of the form $x-2y+z = k$, $x-2y+z = k'$. The first plane contains the point $(1, 0, -5)$, on L, so $k = -4$, and the second plane contains the point $(0, -2, -2)$, on M, so $k' = 2$. The distance between the two planes is, by § 7, $|k-k'|/|\mathbf{c}| = 6/\sqrt{6} = \sqrt{6}$.

Exercises 6.2

1. Two planes (A), (B) each pass through the origin. The plane (A) contains the line

$$\frac{x-1}{2} = \frac{y-2}{3} = \frac{z-3}{2},$$

and the plane (B) contains the line of intersection of the planes

$$x+y+z = 1, \qquad 2x-y+3z = 2.$$

Find the cosine of the angle between the planes (A) and (B).

2. Find the feet of the common perpendicular of the two skew lines

$$x = \frac{y+1}{2} = z, \qquad \frac{x}{2} = \frac{y-2}{-1} = \frac{z+2}{2}.$$

3. A line L is the intersection of the two planes

$$x+y+z = 1, \qquad x-2y+3z = 2.$$

Find the equation of the plane containing L and passing through the origin. Show that the plane just found makes an angle of 60° with the plane $y+z = 0$.

4. Find the equations of the common perpendicular of the skew lines

$$\frac{x+2}{1} = \frac{y}{2} = \frac{z-6}{-1}; \qquad \frac{x+5}{1} = -y = \frac{z}{2},$$

and show that the shortest distance between them is $\sqrt{3}$.

5. Find the angle between the planes

$$3x-4y+5z = 10, \qquad x-4y+3z = 15.$$

Find also the equation of the plane which passes through their line of intersection and is parallel to the line $x = 2y = 3z$.

6. Find the equation of the plane which contains the first of the following two lines and also contains their common perpendicular.

$$\frac{x-1}{2} = -y = -z-1, \qquad x+1 = -\frac{y}{2} = z-3.$$

7. A line L is given by the equations

$$\frac{x}{2} = -(y-1) = \frac{z}{3}.$$

Find the equation of a plane Π parallel to L such that it passes through the line of intersection of the planes

$$3x+y+3z = 0, \qquad x+y+2z = 0.$$

Find the perpendicular distance from L to Π.

8. A line L is the intersection of the two planes

$$x+y+z = 3, \qquad x-2y+3z = 2.$$

Another line M is given by the equations

$$x-1 = y-2 = z-3.$$

Find direction ratios of the line of intersection of the planes joining L and M to the origin.

9. Four points in space have coordinates

A(1, 1, 0), B(3, 0, 1), C(1, 0, 2), D(1, 1, 3).

Find the equations of two parallel planes, of which one contains A and B and the other contains C and D. Deduce the shortest distance between the lines AB, CD.

10. If O is the origin, P the point (1, 2, 3) and L the line of intersection of the planes $x+y = 2$, $z+1 = 0$, find the angle between the plane containing O and L and the plane containing P and L.

11. Find the equation of the plane through the intersection of the

planes

$$2x-y-z = 2, \qquad 3x-2z = 5,$$

which is parallel to the line

$$x = \frac{y}{2} = \frac{z}{3}.$$

Hence deduce the shortest distance between the line and the line of intersection of the first two planes.

12. Two lines are given in space by the following equations:

$$\frac{x}{2} = \frac{y-1}{3} = z, \qquad x+1 = y-2 = \frac{z+4}{2}.$$

Find the equations of the following planes:

(i) the plane containing the first line and parallel to the second,
(ii) the plane containing the second line and parallel to the first,
(iii) the plane containing the first line and passing through the origin,
(iv) the plane containing the first line and the common perpendicular,
(v) the plane containing the second line and the common perpendicular.

13. Find equations of a line with direction vector (1, 2, −3) which meets both the lines

$$\frac{x-2}{5} = \frac{y+1}{3} = \frac{z-3}{2}, \qquad x = y = z.$$

14. Find equations of the projection on the plane

$$6x-3y+2z = 1$$

of the line of intersection of the planes

$$x+y+2z = 3, \qquad 3x+y+3z = 4.$$

15. Show that there are two planes which pass through the line

$$\frac{x-5}{1} = \frac{y-1}{-1} = \frac{z+3}{3}$$

and make an angle of 60 degrees with the plane $y = z$. Find their equations.

16. Find the equation of a line through the origin which meets both the lines given in Question 12 above.

7

OTHER APPLICATIONS

1. Change of coordinate system

One often needs to change from one coordinate system to another. A choice of coordinate system involves two choices, a choice of origin O and a choice of base-vectors $\mathbf{u}_1$, $\mathbf{u}_2$, $\mathbf{u}_3$. The change from one coordinate system (O, $\mathbf{u}_1$, $\mathbf{u}_2$, $\mathbf{u}_3$) to another coordinate system (O′, $\mathbf{u}_1'$, $\mathbf{u}_2'$, $\mathbf{u}_3'$) can therefore be done in two steps. First change the origin O to the new origin O′, keeping the same base-vectors. Second, change the base from $\mathbf{u}_1$, $\mathbf{u}_2$, $\mathbf{u}_3$ to the new base $\mathbf{u}_1'$, $\mathbf{u}_2'$, $\mathbf{u}_3'$, keeping O′ fixed as origin. We now consider the equations governing these two moves.

(*i*) *Alteration of origin*

Let O be the old origin, O′ the new origin and let $\overrightarrow{OO'} = \mathbf{a}$. We wish to find the relation between the position vector $\mathbf{x}$ of a point X relative to O and its position vector $\mathbf{x}'$ relative to O′. From the triangle OO′X we have $\overrightarrow{OX} = \overrightarrow{OO'}+\overrightarrow{O'X}$, that is

$$\mathbf{x} = \mathbf{a}+\mathbf{x}'. \tag{1}$$

In terms of components (x, y, z), this becomes, if $\overrightarrow{OO'} = (a, b, c)$,

$$x = a+x', \quad y = b+y', \quad z = c+z'. \tag{2}$$

(*ii*) *Change of base*

Suppose now that we wish to express our vectors in terms of a new base $\mathbf{u}_1'$, $\mathbf{u}_2'$, $\mathbf{u}_3'$. Let the components of a vector $\mathbf{x}$ referred to the old base be (x_1, x_2, x_3) and let the components of the same vector referred to the new base be x_1', x_2', x_3'. We distinguish between vectors given in terms of components relative to the first base and those given in terms of the second base by the use of round and square brackets. By the definition of components (Chapter 3),

$$\mathbf{x} = x_1'\mathbf{u}_1'+x_2'\mathbf{u}_2'+x_3'\mathbf{u}_3'. \tag{3}$$

Now we must also know the components of the new base-vectors in terms of the old base. Suppose these are as follows:

$$\begin{aligned} \mathbf{u}_1' &= (l_1, m_1, n_1), \\ \mathbf{u}_2' &= (l_2, m_2, n_2), \\ \mathbf{u}_3' &= (l_3, m_3, n_3). \end{aligned}$$

We can now write down the component form of equations (3), referred to the old base-vectors.

$$\begin{aligned} x_1 &= l_1 x_1' + l_2 x_2' + l_3 x_3', \\ x_2 &= m_1 x_1' + m_2 x_2' + m_3 x_3', \\ x_3 &= n_1 x_1' + n_2 x_2' + n_3 x_3'. \end{aligned} \tag{4}$$

These are the equations we want, expressing the old coordinates in terms of the new ones. Of course it is sometimes also necessary to know the equations expressing the new coordinates in terms of the old. One way would be to solve the equations (4) for x_1', x_2', x_3'. However, the following method is simpler. Since l_1 is the $\mathbf{u}_1$-component of $\mathbf{u}_1'$, we have $l_1 = \mathbf{u}_1'.\mathbf{u}_1$. Similarly, $l_2 = \mathbf{u}_2'.\mathbf{u}_1$, $l_3 = \mathbf{u}_3'.\mathbf{u}_1$. Thus, *in the new system*, the components of $\mathbf{u}_1$ are $[l_1, l_2, l_3]$. This and two similar arguments yield

$$\begin{aligned} \mathbf{u}_1 &= [l_1, l_2, l_3], \\ \mathbf{u}_2 &= [m_1, m_2, m_3], \\ \mathbf{u}_3 &= [n_1, n_2, n_3]. \end{aligned}$$

Now, writing $\mathbf{x} = x_1\mathbf{u}_1 + x_2\mathbf{u}_2 + x_3\mathbf{u}_3$ in components referred to the new base, we deduce

$$\left.\begin{aligned} x_1' &= l_1 x_1 + m_1 x_2 + n_1 x_3, \\ x_2' &= l_2 x_1 + m_2 x_2 + n_2 x_3, \\ x_3' &= l_3 x_1 + m_3 x_2 + n_3 x_3. \end{aligned}\right\} \tag{5}$$

Finally, note that the quantities $l_1, \ldots, n_3$ are not arbitrary, because $\mathbf{u}_1'$, $\mathbf{u}_2'$, $\mathbf{u}_3'$ are mutually orthogonal unit vectors and we must have

$$\left.\begin{aligned} l_1^2 + m_1^2 + n_1^2 = l_2^2 + m_2^2 + n_2^2 = l_3^2 + m_3^2 + n_3^2 = 1, \\ l_1 l_2 + m_1 m_2 + n_1 n_2 = l_2 l_3 + m_2 m_3 + n_2 n_3 \\ = l_3 l_1 + m_3 m_1 + n_3 n_1 = 0. \end{aligned}\right\} \tag{6}$$

Exercises

1. Show that $(\frac{2}{3}, \frac{2}{3}, -\frac{1}{3})$, $(\frac{2}{3}, -\frac{1}{3}, \frac{2}{3})$, $(-\frac{1}{3}, \frac{2}{3}, \frac{2}{3})$ form a system of three mutually orthogonal unit vectors. If these are taken as a base for a new coordinate system, with origin unchanged, what is the equation in the new system, of the locus with old equation

$$x^2+xy+xz+z^2 = 1?$$

2. Derive the first equation (5) by multiplying the equations (4) by l_1, m_1, n_1 and adding. (Use relations (6).) Obtain the other two equations (5) by a similar method.

3. Show that, if equations (6) hold, then also

$$l_1^2+l_2^2+l_3^2 = 1, \qquad l_1m_1+l_2m_2+l_3m_3 = 0,$$

together with four similar equations.

4. If $\mathbf{u}_1$, $\mathbf{u}_2$, $\mathbf{u}_3$ are three mutually orthogonal unit vectors forming a right-handed system, fill in the missing components in the table below.

$$\begin{aligned} \mathbf{u}_1 &= (\tfrac{6}{7}, \tfrac{3}{7}, \tfrac{2}{7}), \\ \mathbf{u}_2 &= (\tfrac{3}{7}, -\tfrac{2}{7}, \quad), \\ \mathbf{u}_3 &= (\quad, \quad, \quad). \end{aligned}$$

2. Products of four or more vectors

The formulae for triple products contained in Chapter 5 enable one to transform products involving four or more vectors in a variety of ways and thus to derive vector identities. One example is worked to illustrate the method.

Example. Transform the product $\mathbf{a}\times(\mathbf{b}\times(\mathbf{c}\times\mathbf{d}))$ in two ways.

Solution. (i) Let us denote the above product by $\mathbf{w}$ and let $\mathbf{p} = \mathbf{c}\times\mathbf{d}$. Then, using the vector triple product formula,

$$\begin{aligned} \mathbf{w} = \mathbf{a}\times(\mathbf{b}\times\mathbf{p}) &= (\mathbf{a}.\mathbf{p})\mathbf{b}-(\mathbf{a}.\mathbf{b})\mathbf{p} \\ &= [\mathbf{a}, \mathbf{c}, \mathbf{d}]\mathbf{b}-(\mathbf{a}.\mathbf{b})(\mathbf{c}\times\mathbf{d}). \end{aligned}$$

(ii) Again use the vector triple product formula:

$$\mathbf{b}\times(\mathbf{c}\times\mathbf{d}) = (\mathbf{b}.\mathbf{d})\mathbf{c}-(\mathbf{b}.\mathbf{c})\mathbf{d}.$$

Take vector product with $\mathbf{a}$ on both sides:

$$\mathbf{w} = (\mathbf{b}.\mathbf{d})(\mathbf{a}\times\mathbf{c})-(\mathbf{b}.\mathbf{c})(\mathbf{a}\times\mathbf{d}).$$

If we equate the two expressions obtained for $\mathbf{w}$ and rearrange the resulting equation in a more symmetrical form (remembering that $\mathbf{a}\times\mathbf{d} = -\mathbf{d}\times\mathbf{a}$), we derive

$$[\mathbf{a}, \mathbf{c}, \mathbf{d}]\mathbf{b} = (\mathbf{a}.\mathbf{b})(\mathbf{c}\times\mathbf{d})+(\mathbf{b}.\mathbf{d})(\mathbf{a}\times\mathbf{c})+(\mathbf{b}.\mathbf{c})(\mathbf{d}\times\mathbf{a}). \qquad (7)$$

Exercises

1. If $\mathbf{p} = \mathbf{b}\times\mathbf{c}$, $\mathbf{q} = \mathbf{c}\times\mathbf{a}$, $\mathbf{r} = \mathbf{a}\times\mathbf{b}$, show that $[\mathbf{a}, \mathbf{b}, \mathbf{c}]\mathbf{a} = \mathbf{q}\times\mathbf{r}$, and two similar formulae. Show also that $[\mathbf{p}, \mathbf{q}, \mathbf{r}] = [\mathbf{a}, \mathbf{b}, \mathbf{c}]^2$. Deduce that if $\mathbf{p}, \mathbf{q}, \mathbf{r}$ are known, then $\mathbf{a}, \mathbf{b}, \mathbf{c}$ are determined apart from sign if $[\mathbf{p}, \mathbf{q}, \mathbf{r}] \neq 0$.

2. If $\mathbf{p}+\mathbf{q}+\mathbf{r}+\mathbf{s} = \mathbf{0}$ and $|\mathbf{p}| = |\mathbf{q}| = |\mathbf{r}| = |\mathbf{s}|$, show that $|\mathbf{p}\times\mathbf{q}| = |\mathbf{r}\times\mathbf{s}|$.

3. If $\mathbf{a}, \mathbf{b}, \mathbf{c}$ satisfy the conditions

$$|\mathbf{b}\times\mathbf{c}| = |\mathbf{c}\times\mathbf{a}| = |\mathbf{a}\times\mathbf{b}| = |(\mathbf{a}-\mathbf{b})\times(\mathbf{a}-\mathbf{c})|,$$
$$[\mathbf{a}, \mathbf{b}, \mathbf{c}] \neq 0,$$

deduce from Questions 1, 2 that $|\mathbf{a}| = |\mathbf{b}-\mathbf{c}|$.

Hence show that if the faces of a tetrahedron are all equal in area, then the length of any edge is equal to the length of the opposite edge.

4. Show that $(\mathbf{a}\times\mathbf{b}).(\mathbf{c}\times\mathbf{d}) = (\mathbf{a}.\mathbf{c})(\mathbf{b}.\mathbf{d})-(\mathbf{a}.\mathbf{d})(\mathbf{b}.\mathbf{c})$.

5. Show that

$$\text{(i)}\quad (\mathbf{a}\times\mathbf{b})\times(\mathbf{c}\times\mathbf{d}) = [\mathbf{a}, \mathbf{b}, \mathbf{d}]\mathbf{c}-[\mathbf{a}, \mathbf{b}, \mathbf{c}]\mathbf{d},$$
$$\text{(ii)}\quad (\mathbf{a}\times\mathbf{b})\times(\mathbf{c}\times\mathbf{d}) = [\mathbf{a}, \mathbf{c}, \mathbf{d}]\mathbf{b}-[\mathbf{b}, \mathbf{c}, \mathbf{d}]\mathbf{a}.$$

Deduce that

$$[\mathbf{b}, \mathbf{c}, \mathbf{d}]\mathbf{a}-[\mathbf{a}, \mathbf{c}, \mathbf{d}]\mathbf{b}+[\mathbf{a}, \mathbf{b}, \mathbf{d}]\mathbf{c}-[\mathbf{a}, \mathbf{b}, \mathbf{c}]\mathbf{d} = \mathbf{0}$$

Find an alternative proof of the last formula, using (7).

3. Geometry on the surface of a sphere. Spherical triangles

Let S denote the surface of a sphere centre O and radius r. Thus S is the set of points whose distance from O is equal to the constant r. The geometry on the surface S has great practical importance, because the surface of the earth is almost spherical. If Π is any plane containing O, the intersection of Π with S will be a circle centre O and radius r. Such a circle on S lying in a plane through O is called a *great circle*, since there cannot be a circle of larger radius lying on S. If A, B are two points on S not diametrically opposite, then there is just one great circle containing A and B, given by the intersection of S with the plane OAB. The minor arc of this great circle is the shortest path in S from A to B. Thus the great circles play the same role in geometry on the surface of the sphere as the straight lines do in plane geometry.

A *spherical triangle* is the figure formed on S by three points

A, B, C and the three minor arcs of the great circles BC, CA, AB joining them in pairs. It is assumed that no two of the points A, B, C are diametrically opposite. The angle between the arcs AB, AC at A (that is, the angle between the tangents to these arcs at A) is called *the angle A* and the angles *B*, *C* are similarly defined. In Fig. 30, B′, C′ are the intersections of the great circles AB, AC (produced, if necessary) with the plane B′OC′ through O perpendicular to OA; and AT, AU are the tangents at A to the great circles AB, AC. Since the tangent to a circle is at right angles to the radius it follows that the angle *A* of the spherical triangle is equal to the angle B′OC′, which in turn is equal to the angle be-

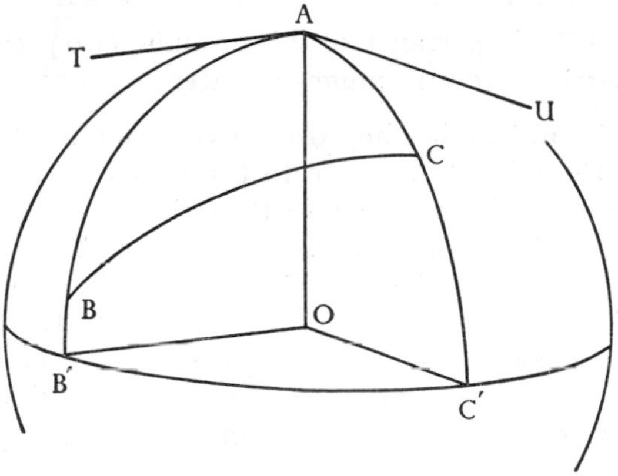

FIG. 30

tween the planes OAB, OAC (see Chapter 6, § 6). Notice however that the angle A is defined with more precision than the angle between two planes, because a normal vector of a plane may be given with a choice of two possible senses (it may point 'above' or 'below' the plane), giving two possible values of the angle which add up to 180°, while the tangents AT, AU will of course be given the sense which is consistent with the direction of travel along the arcs AB, AC in the direction away from A. The angles are always taken to be positive and less than 180°, as in plane trigonometry.

The *sides a, b, c* of the spherical triangle are defined to be the *angles* BOC, COA, AOB subtended at the centre of the sphere. If the actual length of one of the arcs BC, CA, AB is needed, it can always be calculated by multiplying the appropriate angle, measured in radians, by the radius *r* of *S*. Really, in spherical trigonometry, the radius of the sphere is taken as the unit of length. The reader may find this measure of length more natural if he remembers that a similar angular measure is used at sea, the nautical mile being one minute of arc.

4. The cosine rule

The basic problem of spherical trigonometry is, as in plane trigonometry, the solution of triangles. Given three of the quantities a, b, c, A, B, C, to determine the other three. The main formula, from which all the others can be deduced, is the following analogue of the cosine rule:

$$\cos a = \cos b \cos c + \sin b \sin c \cos A. \tag{8}$$

Because of the importance of this formula, two proofs are given (and one further proof is suggested later as an exercise). In the first proof, let **a, b, c** be the position vectors $\overrightarrow{OA}$, $\overrightarrow{OB}$, $\overrightarrow{OC}$ of the vertices of the triangle relative to the centre of the sphere. To avoid unnecessary factors, we take the radius of the sphere to have unit length, so that **a, b, c** are all unit vectors. The vectors $\mathbf{a} \times \mathbf{b}$, $\mathbf{a} \times \mathbf{c}$ are normal to the planes OAB, OAC, and it is easy to see that the angle between them is the angle A, taking the sense of the vectors into account and measuring the angle A as indicated in § 3. Moreover the magnitudes of these vector products are $\sin c$, $\sin b$ respectively. Thus, by the definition of scalar product,

$$(\mathbf{a} \times \mathbf{b}).(\mathbf{a} \times \mathbf{c}) = \sin b \sin c \cos A. \tag{9}$$

We can modify the expression on the left by using the scalar triple product formula $\mathbf{p}.(\mathbf{a} \times \mathbf{c}) = \mathbf{a}.(\mathbf{c} \times \mathbf{p})$. Putting $\mathbf{p} = \mathbf{a} \times \mathbf{b}$ and using also the vector triple product formula, we find

$$\begin{aligned}(\mathbf{a} \times \mathbf{b}).(\mathbf{a} \times \mathbf{c}) &= \mathbf{a}.(\mathbf{c} \times (\mathbf{a} \times \mathbf{b})) = \mathbf{a}.((\mathbf{c}.\mathbf{b})\mathbf{a} - (\mathbf{c}.\mathbf{a})\mathbf{b}) = \\ &= |\mathbf{a}|^2(\mathbf{c}.\mathbf{b}) - (\mathbf{a}.\mathbf{b})(\mathbf{a}.\mathbf{c}) = \cos a - \cos b \cos c \end{aligned} \tag{10}$$

Comparing the two expressions (9), (10), we derive (8).

The second proof of this formula requires the introduction of a coordinate system, and a study of it may help the reader to understand how to choose a coordinate system to suit particular problems. It is helpful to think of the vertex A as the 'North Pole' and the great circle AB as the 'Greenwich Meridian'. The latitudes of the points B, C will be $\frac{1}{2}\pi - c$, $\frac{1}{2}\pi - b$ respectively, and the longitude of C will be the angle A. If the Greenwich Meridian cuts the equator at X and the 90° meridian cuts the equator at Y, we can use

OX, OY, OZ = OA as axes of a rectangular cartesian coordinate system. If we can work out the coordinates of the points B, C in this system, we shall then be able to find the cosine of the angle BOC from the formula for the cosine of the angle between two vectors. (See Chapter **4**.)

Let the great circle AC meet the equator OXY at W. Let BM,

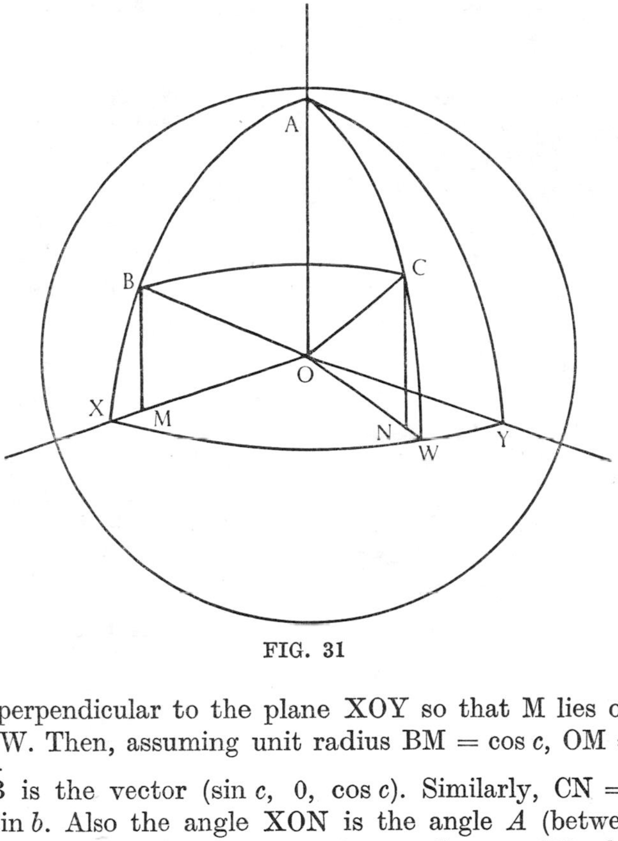

FIG. 31

CN be perpendicular to the plane XOY so that M lies on OX, N on OW. Then, assuming unit radius BM = cos c, OM = sin c and $\overrightarrow{\mathrm{OB}}$ is the vector (sin c, 0, cos c). Similarly, CN = cos b, ON = sin b. Also the angle XON is the angle A (between the planes XOA, WOA). Thus the x- and y-coordinates of N, which are the same as the x- and y-coordinates of C, are ON cos A, ON sin A, and the coordinates of C are

$$\overrightarrow{\mathrm{OC}} = (\sin b \cos A, \sin b \sin A, \cos b).$$

Using the formula for scalar product in terms of components,

((8) p. 52), we have

$$\cos a = \overrightarrow{OB}.\overrightarrow{OC} = \sin b \sin c \cos A + \cos b \cos c, \tag{8}$$

as desired.

5. Worked example

The usefulness of the cosine rule will be illustrated and the principle behind the second proof made clearer by a study of the following example.

Assuming the earth to be a sphere of radius 3 963 miles, find the distance from New York (40° 40′ N., 73° 50′ W.) *to Moscow* (55° 45′ N., 37° 42′ E.).

Take the spherical triangle ABC with A at the North Pole, B at New York, C at Moscow. The arc from the North Pole to any point in the Northern Hemisphere subtends an angle $90°-l$, where l is the latitude. Thus, in the given spherical triangle,

$$b = 34°\ 15', \qquad c = 49°\ 20'.$$

Since New York is West of Greenwich and Moscow is East, the angle A is the sum of their longitudes, so $A = 111°\ 32'$. For the side a, representing the distance we want, the cosine rule gives $\cos a = \cos 34°\ 15' \cos 49°\ 20' - \sin 34°\ 15' \sin 49°\ 20' \sin 21°\ 32'$. (To come within the range of the tables, which run from 0 to 90°, use the relation $\cos A = \cos(90°+21°\ 32') = -\sin 21°\ 32'$.)

We calculate each of the products with logarithms, and subtract to find cos a. The details are below.

log cos 34° 15′ = 1·9172	log sin 34° 15′ = 1·7504	0·5386
log cos 49° 20′ = 1·8140	log sin 49° 20′ = 1·8799	0·1567
1·7312	log sin 21° 32′ = 1·5647	0·3819
product = 0·5386	1·1950	
	product = 0·1567	

Hence $\cos a = 0{\cdot}3819$ and $a = 67°\ 33'$. In radian measure, $a = 67\frac{33}{60}\times\frac{\pi}{180}$, and the distance required is

$$\frac{67\frac{33}{60}\times 3{\cdot}1416\times 3963}{180} = 4\ 672 \text{ miles.}$$

6. The sine rule

Another useful formula which can be established with the aid of vectors is the sine rule:

$$\frac{\sin a}{\sin A} = \frac{\sin b}{\sin B} = \frac{\sin c}{\sin C}. \tag{11}$$

As in § 5, let **a**, **b**, **c** denote the position vectors, relative to the centre of the sphere, of the three vertices of the spherical triangle. The magnitude of the vector product $(\mathbf{a}\times\mathbf{b})\times(\mathbf{a}\times\mathbf{c})$ is $\sin b \sin c \sin A$, since the magnitudes of $\mathbf{a}\times\mathbf{b}$, $\mathbf{a}\times\mathbf{c}$ are $\sin c$, $\sin b$, and A is the angle between them. Now, by the vector triple product formula,

$$(\mathbf{a}\times\mathbf{b})\times(\mathbf{a}\times\mathbf{c}) = ((\mathbf{a}\times\mathbf{b}).\mathbf{c})\mathbf{a}-((\mathbf{a}\times\mathbf{b}).\mathbf{a})\mathbf{c} = [\mathbf{a}, \mathbf{b}, \mathbf{c}]\mathbf{a}.$$

Since **a** is a unit vector the magnitude of this expression is $|[\mathbf{a}, \mathbf{b}, \mathbf{c}]|$, and, by symmetry, we deduce

$$|[\mathbf{a}, \mathbf{b}, \mathbf{c}]| = \sin b \sin c \sin A = \sin c \sin a \sin B = \sin a \sin b \sin C,$$

from which (11) follows.

An alternative geometrical proof for (11) may be found interesting (Fig. 32). Drop a perpendicular AL on the plane BOC and drop

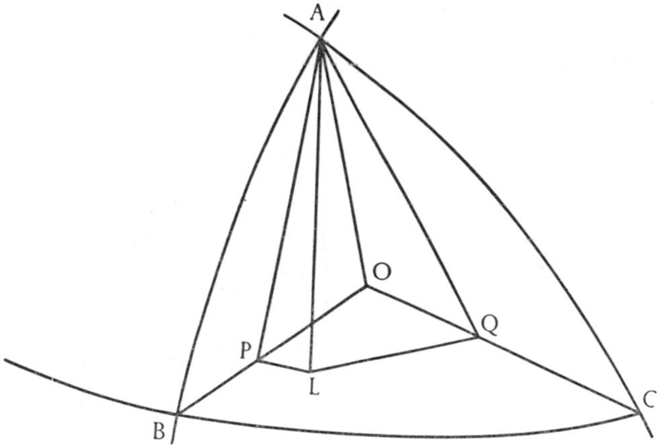

FIG. 32

LP, LQ perpendicular to OB, OC respectively. Then the plane APL is at right angles to OB, because the lines AL, LP are. Similarly the plane AQL is at right angles to OC. Since AP, PL are both at right angles to OB, the angle APL is the angle B of the spherical triangle and similarly the angle AQL is the angle C.

From the right-angled triangles OPA, ALP,

$$\text{AL} = \text{AP} \sin B = \text{OA} \sin c \sin B.$$

By a similar argument, $\text{AL} = \text{OA} \sin b \sin C$, and (11) follows.

7. The polar spherical triangle

If a great circle is given on the sphere, the two points where the line through the centre perpendicular to the plane of the great circle cuts the sphere are called the *poles* of the great circle. If, for example, the sphere is the earth and the great circle is the equator, then its poles are the North and South Geographical Poles. If ABC is a spherical triangle, let P be that pole of the great circle BC which lies on the same side of this great circle as A lies. The angle POA is then an acute angle. Let the poles Q, R of CA, AB be similarly defined. The spherical triangle PQR is said to be the *polar spherical triangle* of ABC. If **p, q, r** are the position vectors of P, Q, R and **a, b, c** those of A, B, C, then we have the relations

$$\begin{array}{lll} \mathbf{p}.\mathbf{a} > 0 & \mathbf{p}.\mathbf{b} = 0 & \mathbf{p}.\mathbf{c} = 0, \\ \mathbf{q}.\mathbf{a} = 0 & \mathbf{q}.\mathbf{b} > 0 & \mathbf{q}.\mathbf{c} = 0, \\ \mathbf{r}.\mathbf{a} = 0 & \mathbf{r}.\mathbf{b} = 0 & \mathbf{r}.\mathbf{c} > 0. \end{array}$$

It follows from the symmetry of these defining relations that, *if* PQR *is the polar triangle of* ABC, *then* ABC *is the polar triangle of* PQR.

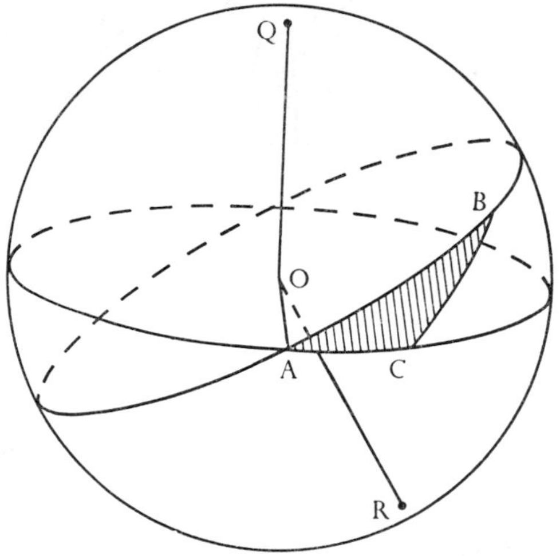

FIG. 33

The angle A is the angle between the planes OAB, OAC, and OQ, OR are normal vectors of these planes. The angle A is therefore equal either to the angle QOR, or to $\pi-$QOR. Consideration of Fig. 33 will convince the reader that the second is the correct expression. Now the angle QOR is, by definition, a *side* of the polar triangle. Thus the three sides of the polar triangle are $\pi-A$, $\pi-B$, $\pi-C$. Because ABC is also the polar triangle of PQR, we deduce in the same way that the angles of PQR are $\pi-a$, $\pi-b$, $\pi-c$. These facts enable us to derive a new formula from any known formula in spherical trigonometry by putting $\pi-A$, $\pi-B$, $\pi-C$, $\pi-a$, $\pi-b$, $\pi-c$ instead of a, b, c, A, B, C respectively. For example, if we apply the cosine rule (8) to the polar spherical triangle we obtain

$$-\cos A = \cos B \cos C - \sin B \sin C \cos a.$$

8. The area of a spherical triangle

It is known that the area of the surface of a sphere of unit radius is 4π. Now consider the area of a *segment* of the sphere bounded by two great semicircles which meet at an angle θ. It is clear that this

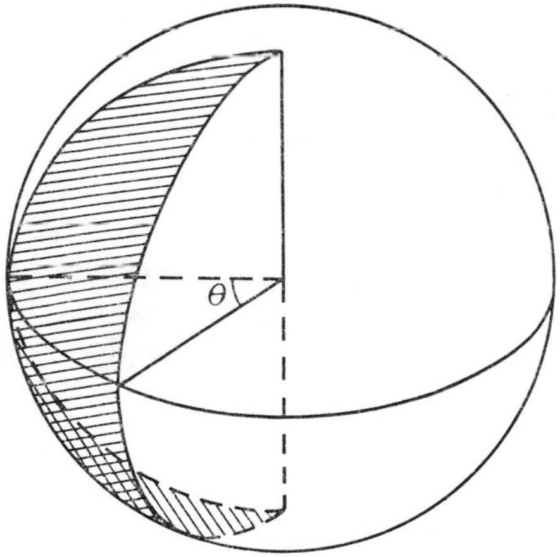

FIG. 34 Area of a segment is proportional to the angle θ.

area is proportional to θ, and when $\theta = \pi$, it is half the area of the sphere. Thus the area of such a segment is 2θ.

Now consider a spherical triangle ABC. Let A′, B′, C′ be the points diametrically opposite to A, B, C on the surface of the sphere. The three great circles ABA′B′, BCB′C′, CAC′A′ subdivide the surface of the sphere into the eight triangular regions listed below (Fig. 35).

ABC, A′BC, AB′C, ABC′,
A′B′C′, AB′C′, A′BC′, A′B′C.

Each triangle is diametrically opposite to the one listed below it, and therefore has the same area. Let x, y, z, w denote the four areas in order. The first and second triangles in the top row taken

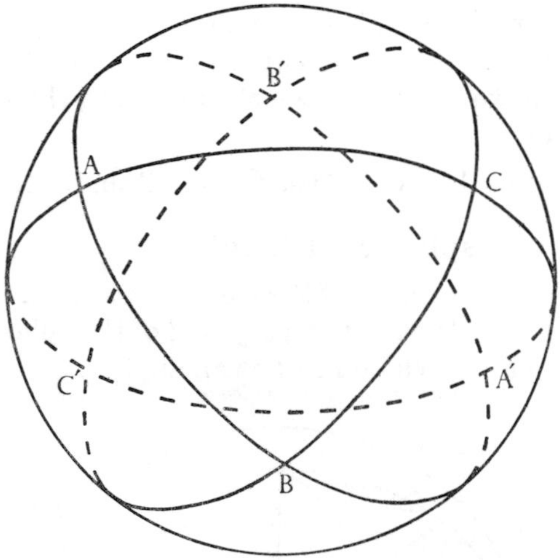

FIG. 35 Subdivision of the surface of the sphere into eight triangular portions by three great circles.

together form a segment with angle A. Hence, by the formula just found for the area of a segment, $x+y = 2A$. Similarly $x+z = 2B$, $x+w = 2C$. Again, since the sum of all the eight areas is the whole surface of the sphere, $x+y+z+w = 2\pi$. If we add together the first three equations just found and subtract the last one we obtain $x = A+B+C-\pi$.

The area of a spherical triangle is the excess of the sum of its angles over π.

Exercises on Spherical Trigonometry

1. In Fig. 30 let **b**, **c**, **b′**, **c′**, **a** be the position vectors relative to the centre of the sphere of the points B, C, B′, C′, A. Show that

$$\mathbf{b} = \cos c\,\mathbf{a}+\sin c\,\mathbf{b}', \quad \mathbf{c} = \cos b\,\mathbf{a}+\sin b\,\mathbf{c}',$$

and that $\mathbf{b}.\mathbf{c} = \cos a$, $\qquad \mathbf{b}'.\mathbf{c}' = \cos A$.

Deduce the cosine rule.

(This proof was given in a terminal examination by a first-year student of engineering at Queen's College, Dundee.)

2. Deduce the sine rule from the cosine rule by using (8) and the identity $\sin^2 A = 1-\cos^2 A$.

3. In an equilateral spherical triangle whose sides are all equal to a and whose angles are all equal to A, show that

$$\cos a = \cos A+\cos a \cos A,$$

$$4\cos^2 \tfrac{1}{2}a \sin^2 \tfrac{1}{2}A = 1.$$

4. Show that if $s = \tfrac{1}{2}(a+b+c)$ then

$$\cos^2 \tfrac{1}{2}A = \frac{\sin s \sin (s-a)}{\sin b \sin c},$$

$$\sin^2 \tfrac{1}{2}A = \frac{\sin (s-b) \sin (s-c)}{\sin b \sin c},$$

$$\tan^2 \tfrac{1}{2}A = \frac{\sin (s-b) \sin (s-c)}{\sin s \sin (s-a)}.$$

5. If $C = \tfrac{1}{2}\pi$, prove the formulae

$$\cos c = \cos a \cos b,$$

$$\cos A \tan c = \tan b,$$

$$\sin A \sin c = \sin a,$$

$$\tan a = \tan A \sin b,$$

$$\cos A = \cos a \sin B.$$

6. If α, β, γ are the angles between the line OA and the plane BOC, between the line OB and the plane COA, and between the line OC and the plane AOB respectively, show that

$$\sin a \sin \alpha = \sin b \sin \beta = \sin c \sin \gamma = \sin b \sin c \sin A,$$

$$\sin^2 a \cos^2 \alpha = \cos^2 b+\cos^2 c-2\cos a \cos b \cos c.$$

9. The tetrahedron

If ABCD is a tetrahedron, one may wish to know the values of various quantities associated with the figure, for instance:

(i) the six lengths BC, CA, AB, AD, BD, CD;
(ii) the twelve angles of the four plane triangular faces;
(iii) the six angles between pairs of plane faces;
(iv) the three shortest distances between pairs of opposite edges;
(v) the angle between a face and an edge not contained in it;

(vi) the volume;
(vii) the area of the plane faces.

These quantities are by no means independent, since, for instance, if we know the lengths of the sides of a plane triangular face we can deduce the angles and area by the methods of ordinary trigonometry. In fact, there are only six independent constants needed to define a tetrahedron, so if we take any seven of the quantities above, there must be a relation between them. It is useful to take one of the vertices, say, D, as origin, and work in terms of the vectors $\overrightarrow{DA} = \mathbf{a}$, $\overrightarrow{DB} = \mathbf{b}$, $\overrightarrow{DC} = \mathbf{c}$. A knowledge of the six quantities

$$|\mathbf{a}|^2,\ |\mathbf{b}|^2,\ |\mathbf{c}|^2,\ \mathbf{b}.\mathbf{c},\ \mathbf{c}.\mathbf{a},\ \mathbf{a}.\mathbf{b} \tag{12}$$

will enable us to calculate all the other quantities listed above. Notice that the quantities (12) can be obtained at once from equations of the type

$$2\mathbf{b}.\mathbf{c} = |\mathbf{b}|^2+|\mathbf{c}|^2-|\mathbf{b}-\mathbf{c}|^2$$

if we know the lengths of the six sides.

As an instance, let us show how to express the volume V in terms of the quantities (12). The volume of a tetrahedron is known to be one-third of the area of the base multiplied by the height, so $6V = \mathbf{a}.(\mathbf{b}\times\mathbf{c})$. Now

$$|\mathbf{a}.(\mathbf{b}\times\mathbf{c})|^2 = |\mathbf{a}|^2|\mathbf{b}\times\mathbf{c}|^2-|\mathbf{a}\times(\mathbf{b}\times\mathbf{c})|^2.$$

Simplifying this with the help of the vector triple product formula,

$$36V^2 = |\mathbf{a}|^2|\mathbf{b}|^2|\mathbf{c}|^2-\sum|\mathbf{a}|^2(\mathbf{b}.\mathbf{c})^2+2(\mathbf{b}.\mathbf{c})(\mathbf{c}.\mathbf{a})(\mathbf{a}.\mathbf{b}) \tag{13}$$

Here the $\sum$ sign denotes summation over all the expressions derived from the given one by cyclic interchange of the letters **a**, **b**, **c**.

As another example, let us take the shortest distance between the two opposite edges DA, BC. The line DA is given parametrically by the equation

$$\mathbf{x} = t\mathbf{a}, \tag{14}$$

and the line BC is given parametrically by

$$\mathbf{y} = \mathbf{b}+u(\mathbf{b}-\mathbf{c}). \tag{15}$$

(By this we mean, as in Chapter 6, that any point on DA has a position vector $\mathbf{x}$ given by (14), with a suitable choice of the real number t, and any point on BC has a position vector $\mathbf{y}$ given by (15), with a suitable choice of the real number u. Notice that we have to use different letters for the coordinate vectors $\mathbf{x}$, $\mathbf{y}$, because, of course, the points are not the same, and similarly we need different letters for the two parameters t, u.) Suppose now that t, u are given values in (14), (15) so that $\mathbf{x}$, $\mathbf{y}$ are the feet of the common perpendicular, which will happen if $\mathbf{x}-\mathbf{y}$ is parallel to $\mathbf{a}\times(\mathbf{b}-\mathbf{c})$, the vector product of the direction vectors of the two lines. We thus have

$$\mathbf{x}-\mathbf{y} = k(\mathbf{a}\times(\mathbf{b}-\mathbf{c}))$$

or

$$t\mathbf{a}-\mathbf{b}-u(\mathbf{b}-\mathbf{c}) = k(\mathbf{a}\times(\mathbf{b}-\mathbf{c})). \tag{16}$$

In (16), take scalar product with $\mathbf{a}\times(\mathbf{b}-\mathbf{c})$ on both sides. We deduce that

$$k\,|\,\mathbf{a}\times(\mathbf{b}-\mathbf{c})\,|^2 = -\mathbf{b}.(\mathbf{a}\times(\mathbf{b}-\mathbf{c})) = \mathbf{b}.(\mathbf{a}\times\mathbf{c}) = \pm 6V.$$

Thus

$$|\,\mathbf{x}-\mathbf{y}\,| = |\,k\,|\,|\,\mathbf{a}\times(\mathbf{b}-\mathbf{c})\,| = \frac{6V}{|\,\mathbf{a}\times(\mathbf{b}-\mathbf{c})\,|}. \tag{17}$$

We have already seen how to express V in terms of the quantities (12) and the denominator in (17) can be expressed in terms of them too by the use of the formula $|\,\mathbf{p}\times\mathbf{q}\,|^2 = |\,\mathbf{p}\,|^2\,|\,\mathbf{q}\,|^2-(\mathbf{p}.\mathbf{q})^2$. In geometrical terms, the formula (17) states:

The shortest distance between two opposite edges of a tetrahedron is equal to six times the volume divided by the product of the lengths of the edges concerned multiplied by the sine of the angle between them.

If one wishes to work out angles between faces of the tetrahedron, the formulae of spherical trigonometry are helpful. For let us consider the three plane faces that meet at the vertex A, and imagine them produced indefinitely beyond the points B, C, D. The three planes will cut out a spherical triangle on the sphere with unit radius centre A, and the three sides of this spherical triangle will be the angles BAC, CAD, DAB while its three angles will be the angles between the faces of the tetrahedron which meet at A.

To illustrate all these points, we evaluate some of these quantities when ABCD is a *regular* tetrahedron, that is one with all its faces equilateral triangles. If l is the length of one of its edges, then, since all the angles between intersecting edges are $\frac{1}{3}\pi$, and we have

$$|\mathbf{a}|^2 = |\mathbf{b}|^2 = |\mathbf{c}|^2 = l^2, \qquad \mathbf{b}.\mathbf{c} = \mathbf{c}.\mathbf{a} = \mathbf{a}.\mathbf{b} = \tfrac{1}{2}l^2.$$

For the volume V we find, from (13), $6V = l^3/\sqrt{2}$. To derive the shortest distance between a pair of opposite edges, we note the fact that, in this case $\mathbf{a}.\mathbf{b} = \mathbf{a}.\mathbf{c}$ and $\mathbf{a}$ is at right angles to $\mathbf{b}-\mathbf{c}$. Thus $|\mathbf{a}\times(\mathbf{b}-\mathbf{c})| = |\mathbf{a}||\mathbf{b}-\mathbf{c}| = l^2$. Substituting in (17) we see that the shortest distance is $l/\sqrt{2}$. Finally, to find the angle α between two faces we use the formula

$$\cos a = \cos b \cos c + \sin b \sin c \cos\alpha.$$

In this case we have a spherical triangle with $a = b = c = \tfrac{1}{3}\pi$, so

$$\frac{1}{2} = \frac{1}{2}.\frac{1}{2} + \frac{\sqrt{3}}{2}.\frac{\sqrt{3}}{2}\cos\alpha, \quad \text{and} \quad \cos\alpha = \tfrac{1}{3}.$$

By symmetry, the centroid (Chapter 2, § 15) $\mathbf{g} = \tfrac{1}{4}(\mathbf{a}+\mathbf{b}+\mathbf{c})$ of a regular tetrahedron is equidistant from the four vertices. This can be verified by evaluating the lengths:

$$|\mathbf{g}|^2 = \frac{1}{16}\Big(\sum|\mathbf{a}|^2 + 2\sum\mathbf{b}.\mathbf{c}\Big) = \tfrac{3}{8}l^2,$$

$$|\mathbf{g}-\mathbf{a}|^2 = \frac{1}{16}\Big(|\mathbf{b}+\mathbf{c}|^2 - 6(\mathbf{b}+\mathbf{c}).\mathbf{a} + 9|\mathbf{a}|^2\Big) = \tfrac{3}{8}l^2$$

For applications in chemistry, it is useful to know the angle θ subtended at the centroid by the edge DA. We have

$$\tfrac{3}{8}l^2\cos\theta = \mathbf{g}.(\mathbf{g}-\mathbf{a}) = -\tfrac{1}{8}l^2.$$

Thus $\qquad \cos\theta = -\tfrac{1}{3}, \qquad \theta = \pi - \cos^{-1}\tfrac{1}{3}.$

Exercises on the tetrahedron

1. Show that the points $(0, 0, 0)$, $(0, a, a)$, $(a, 0, a)$, $(a, a, 0)$ are the vertices of a regular tetrahedron of side $a\sqrt{2}$. Find, by the methods of coordinate geometry, its volume, the angles between its faces and the shortest distance between pairs of opposite edges, thus verifying the results obtained at the end of the last paragraph.

2. The lengths of the edges of a tetrahedron are $BC = 3$, $CA = 3$, $AB = 5$, $AD = BD = CD = 4$. Find its volume and the shortest distances between pairs of opposite edges.

3. Let l, l'; m, m'; n, n' be the lengths of the three pairs of opposite edges of a tetrahedron. Let θ be the angle between the edges of length l, l'. Show that

$$2ll' \cos\theta = m^2+m'^2-(n^2+n'^2).$$

4. If **0**, **a**, **b**, **c** are the vertices of a tetrahedron, show that the position vector **x** of the centre of the circumscribing sphere is given by the equation

$$[\mathbf{a}, \mathbf{b}, \mathbf{c}]\mathbf{x} = \tfrac{1}{2}|\mathbf{a}|^2(\mathbf{b}\times\mathbf{c})+\tfrac{1}{2}|\mathbf{b}|^2(\mathbf{c}\times\mathbf{a})+\tfrac{1}{2}|\mathbf{c}|^2(\mathbf{a}\times\mathbf{b}).$$

10. The cube

The solid figure known as a *cube*, which has six square faces, is more important than the other regular solids because cubes can be stacked so as to fill space. A glance at the diagram shows that the cube has

(i) six square faces falling into three pairs of parallel *opposite* faces,
(ii) eight vertices,
(iii) twelve edges, falling into three sets of four parallel edges.

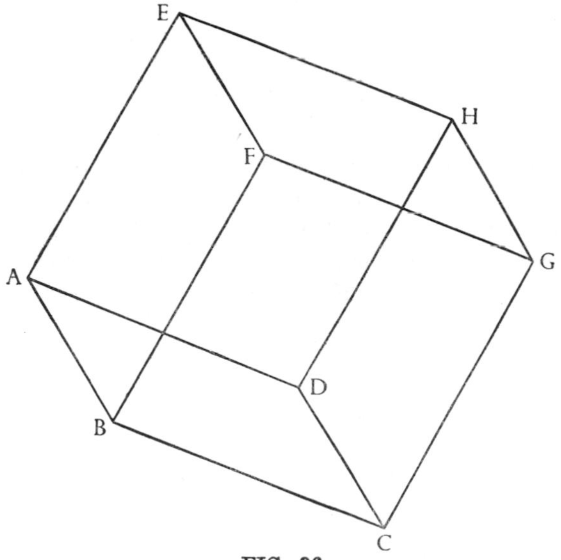

FIG. 36

Each vertex lies on three edges and on three faces. Each edge lies on two faces and contains two vertices. Each face has four edges and four vertices. Two vertices of a cube are called *opposite* if they do not belong to any common face. If V is a vertex the opposite vertex V′ is the intersection of the three faces opposite to the three which meet at V. In Fig. 36, A and G, B and H, C and E, D and F are pairs of opposite vertices.

The line joining two vertices, if it is not an edge, is called a *diagonal.* If the two vertices belong to one face, the diagonal is called a *face diagonal.* A diagonal joining two opposite vertices is called a *body diagonal.*

Since the three edge-directions are mutually perpendicular, it is natural to choose a coordinate system in which these are the directions of the base-vectors. For symmetry, we chose the origin of coordinates to be at the *centre* of the cube—the point of intersection of three planes each parallel to a pair of faces and lying midway between them. If the length of an edge of the cube is $2a$, the equations of the plane faces are

$$x = a, \quad x = -a, \quad y = a, \quad y = -a, \quad z = a, \quad z = -a.$$

The coordinates of the vertices are $(\pm a, \pm a, \pm a)$, $2 \times 2 \times 2 = 8$ choices of sign giving eight vertices in all. The equations of the twelve edges are

$$\begin{aligned} \pm x &= \pm y = a, \\ \pm y &= \pm z = a, \\ \pm z &= \pm x = a. \end{aligned}$$

The equations of the other points, lines and planes associated with the cube can be worked out from these by using the methods of coordinate geometry. Some possibilities are suggested in the following exercises, but the reader may find others which we have missed. It may be found helpful to have a wooden or cardboard model of a cube to help in tuition.

Exercises on the cube

(Unless otherwise indicated, the cube referred to in these exercises will have side $2a$ and the coordinate system will be the one described in the last paragraph.)

1. The equation of the three face diagonals through (a, a, a) are

$$x = y, \quad z = a; \qquad y = z, \quad x = a; \qquad z = x, \quad y = a.$$

2. The equations of the body diagonals are $x = \pm y = \pm z$.

3. How many face diagonals are there? How many body diagonals?

4. If d is a given body diagonal, how many face diagonals meet it? How many face diagonals are skew to it? Show that the shortest distance between a face diagonal and a body diagonal skew to it is $a\sqrt{2}/\sqrt{3}$.

5. All the body diagonals bisect one another at the origin.

6. How would you define a pair of *opposite edges* of a cube?

7. If f is a given face diagonal, how many body diagonals meet f? How many other face diagonals meet f? How many face diagonals are parallel to f? How many are skew to f?

8. Show that a face diagonal is at right angles to any body diagonal which is skew to it. Show also that the face diagonals skew to a given body diagonal form the sides of two equilateral triangles.

9. If two face diagonals are skew to one another, show that either (i) they lie in opposite faces and are at right angles to one another or (ii) they lie in adjacent faces and the angle between them is 60°. Find the shortest distance between them in each case.

10. A cube has its centre at the origin and two of its adjacent vertices are $(5, -1, -1)$ and $(3, 3, 3)$. Find all its vertices.

11. The eight vertices of a cube fall into two sets of four, each set being the vertices of a regular tetrahedron. No two vertices in the same set are adjacent vertices of the cube. Each edge of one of these two tetrahedra is a face diagonal of the cube. If one of the two inscribed tetrahedra is known, the cube is uniquely determined.

SOLUTIONS TO THE EXERCISES

In all solutions, unless otherwise stated, points A, X, &c., will have position vectors denoted by the corresponding small letters **a**, **x**, &c. Whenever a point is labelled O in the question as set, this point will be taken as origin unless the contrary is explicitly stated.

Exercises page 20

1. $|\mathbf{a}|-|\mathbf{b}|$.

2. (i) The vectors $\mathbf{a}+\mathbf{b}$, $\mathbf{b}+\mathbf{a}$ then have the same direction and sense (that of **a** and **b**) and their magnitudes $|\mathbf{a}|+|\mathbf{b}|$, $|\mathbf{b}|+|\mathbf{a}|$ are equal, by number-algebra. (ii) Assume, interchanging **a** and **b** if necessary, that $|\mathbf{b}|<|\mathbf{a}|$. As in Q. 1, it can be seen that $\mathbf{a}+\mathbf{b}$ and $\mathbf{b}+\mathbf{a}$ are both vectors with the same direction and sense as **a** and magnitude $|\mathbf{a}|-|\mathbf{b}|$. (iii) follows from the equations $\mathbf{a}+\mathbf{0}=\mathbf{a}=\mathbf{0}+\mathbf{a}$ (p. 19).

Exercises on Chapter 2 page 34

1. $-\mathbf{a}+\mathbf{b}$, $2\mathbf{a}+\mathbf{b}$, $-2\mathbf{a}+2\mathbf{b}$, $3\mathbf{a}$, $-\mathbf{a}+\mathbf{b}$, $-4\mathbf{a}+\mathbf{b}$. Midpoints $\frac{1}{2}(\mathbf{a}+\mathbf{b})$, $\frac{3}{2}\mathbf{a}+\mathbf{b}$, $\mathbf{a}+\frac{3}{2}\mathbf{b}$, $\mathbf{b}$. Centroids $\frac{1}{3}(4\mathbf{a}+2\mathbf{b})$, $\mathbf{a}+\mathbf{b}$, $\frac{1}{3}(2\mathbf{a}+4\mathbf{b})$.

2. $\mathbf{a}+\mathbf{c}-\mathbf{b}$.

3. The midpoint of OR is also the midpoint of PQ since POQR is a parallelogram. $\overrightarrow{OM}=\frac{1}{2}\mathbf{OR}=\frac{1}{2}(\mathbf{p}+\mathbf{q})$.

4. $\mathbf{l}+\mathbf{m}+\mathbf{n}=\frac{1}{2}(\mathbf{b}+\mathbf{c})+\frac{1}{2}(\mathbf{c}+\mathbf{a})+\frac{1}{2}(\mathbf{a}+\mathbf{b})=\mathbf{a}+\mathbf{b}+\mathbf{c}$.
$\overrightarrow{AL}+\overrightarrow{BM}+\overrightarrow{CN}=\mathbf{l}-\mathbf{a}+\mathbf{m}-\mathbf{b}+\mathbf{n}-\mathbf{c}=\mathbf{0}$.

5. $3\,\overrightarrow{GG'}=3(\mathbf{g}'-\mathbf{g})=\mathbf{a}'+\mathbf{b}'+\mathbf{c}'-(\mathbf{a}+\mathbf{b}+\mathbf{c})=\overrightarrow{AA'}+\overrightarrow{BB'}+\overrightarrow{CC'}$.

6. The midpoint of PR has position vector

$$\tfrac{1}{2}(\mathbf{p}+\mathbf{r})=\tfrac{1}{6}(\mathbf{a}+\mathbf{b}+\mathbf{c}+\mathbf{d}+\mathbf{e}+\mathbf{f})$$

$=\frac{1}{2}(\mathbf{q}+\mathbf{s})$, the position vector of the midpoint of QS. Thus PQRS is a parallelogram.

7. As in Ex. 1, p. 31, it can be shown that PR, QS, TU all have the same midpoint. Thus PQRS, PTRU, QTSU are all parallelograms.

8. Let P, Q, R, S (position vectors $\mathbf{p}, \mathbf{q}, \mathbf{r}, \mathbf{s}$) be the centroids of BCD, CDA, DAB, ABC, in order. The position vector of the point dividing AP in the ratio 3 : 1 is $\frac{1}{4}(\mathbf{a}+3\mathbf{p}) = \frac{1}{4}(\mathbf{a}+\mathbf{b}+\mathbf{c}+\mathbf{d})$. This is the point G, G lies on AP and similarly G lies on BQ, CR, DS, so these lines meet at G. By (11), p. 30, $\mathbf{a}' = \frac{1}{4}(3\mathbf{a}+\mathbf{d})$, $\mathbf{b}' = \frac{1}{4}(3\mathbf{b}+\mathbf{d})$, $\mathbf{c}' = \frac{1}{4}(3\mathbf{c}+\mathbf{d})$, so the centroid of A′B′C′ has position vector

$$\tfrac{1}{3}(\mathbf{a}'+\mathbf{b}'+\mathbf{c}') = \tfrac{1}{4}(\mathbf{a}+\mathbf{b}+\mathbf{c}+\mathbf{d}) = \mathbf{g}.$$

9. Since ABCD, A′B′C′D′ are parallelograms, we have $\mathbf{b}-\mathbf{a} = \mathbf{c}-\mathbf{d}$, $\mathbf{b}'-\mathbf{a}' = \mathbf{c}'-\mathbf{d}'$. Adding these two equations and dividing by 2 we find $\frac{1}{2}(\mathbf{b}+\mathbf{b}')-\frac{1}{2}(\mathbf{a}+\mathbf{a}') = \frac{1}{2}(\mathbf{c}+\mathbf{c}')-\frac{1}{2}(\mathbf{d}+\mathbf{d}')$, i.e., the four midpoints form a parallelogram.

10. Take O as origin. By § 8, § 14, $\overrightarrow{OH} = \mathbf{a}+\mathbf{b}+\mathbf{c} = 3\,\overrightarrow{OG}$.

11. $\overrightarrow{CD} = -\mathbf{p}+\mathbf{q}$, $\overrightarrow{DE} = -\mathbf{p}$, $\overrightarrow{EF} = -\mathbf{q}$, $\overrightarrow{FA} = \mathbf{p}-\mathbf{q}$. $\overrightarrow{OA} = -\mathbf{q}$, $\overrightarrow{OB} = \mathbf{p}-\mathbf{q}$, $\overrightarrow{OC} = \mathbf{p}$. Since O is the circumcentre of the triangle ABC, its orthocentre has position vector (§ 8) $\mathbf{a}+\mathbf{b}+\mathbf{c} = 2\mathbf{b}$. Similarly the orthocentre of BCD has position vector $2\mathbf{c}$, &c. Thus the orthocentres lie on a circle centre O and radius $2r$.

12. Let M be the midpoint of CD. Then

$$\overrightarrow{MP} = \tfrac{1}{2}(\mathbf{a}+\mathbf{b}+\mathbf{c}+\mathbf{d})-\tfrac{1}{2}(\mathbf{c}+\mathbf{d}) = \tfrac{1}{2}(\mathbf{a}+\mathbf{b}).$$

Since $|\,\mathbf{a}\,| = |\,\mathbf{b}\,|$, this is at right angles to $\mathbf{b}-\mathbf{a} = \overrightarrow{AB}$.

13. Since $|\,A_2B_1\,| = |\,\mathbf{a}_3\,| = 1$, and $|\,A_3B_1\,| = |\,\mathbf{a}_2\,| = 1$, the point B_1 is centre of a unit circle through A_2, A_3. Similarly $\mathbf{b}_2 = \mathbf{a}_3+\mathbf{a}_1$, $\mathbf{b}_3 = \mathbf{a}_1+\mathbf{a}_2$. Then $\overrightarrow{B_1C} = \mathbf{a}_1$, $\overrightarrow{B_2C} = \mathbf{a}_2$, $\overrightarrow{B_3C} = \mathbf{a}_3$. Since these are unit vectors, the three circles of unit radius with centres at B_1, B_2, B_3 intersect at C.

Exercises on Chapter 3 page 48

1. (0, −2, 11), (−7, 9, −4), (−9, 10, −14), (−1, 1, 1).

2. (i) (2, 1, 0); (ii) (0, 1, −2); (iii) (−1, 1, 0); (iv) (1, 1, 1).

3. P(3, 0, −1), Q(0, 3, 2), $\overrightarrow{QP} = (3, -3, -3)$, $\overrightarrow{QB} = (2, -4, -2)$, $\overrightarrow{BP} = (1, 1, -1)$. Hence $QP^2 = 27 = QB^2+BP^2$, and BPQ is a right angle.

4. $p = 0$, $q = r = 1$.

5. If **a** and **b** are at right angles, then by Pythagoras's Theorem, since **a**+**b** represents the hypotenuse, we have

$$|\mathbf{a}|^2+|\mathbf{b}|^2=|\mathbf{a}+\mathbf{b}|^2.$$

Written out in components, this simplifies to the result given.

6. (i) Collinear, $-\frac{1}{3}$; (ii) collinear, $-\frac{3}{4}$; (iii) not collinear.

7. (1, 6, 5).

8. M is (2, 1, 0). Hence $\overrightarrow{AM}=(-1,-2,-1)$, length $\sqrt{6}$, $\overrightarrow{BM}=(1,1,1)$, length $\sqrt{3}$, AB $=(-2,-1,-2)$, length 3. $AB^2=AM^2+MB^2$.

9. Centroid is $(\frac{5}{3}, -\frac{5}{3})$. In the new system A $(4, -2)$, B $(-2, -4)$. C $(-3, -1)$, G $(-\frac{1}{3}, -\frac{7}{3})$.

10. $\cos\theta=2/\sqrt{5}$, $\sin\theta=1/\sqrt{5}$; $(41/\sqrt{5}, 2/\sqrt{5})$, $(34/\sqrt{5}, -2/\sqrt{5})$,

11. (i) $x'^2+y'^2=1$. (ii) $x'^2+y'^2+\sqrt{2}x'+1=0$. (iii) $2x'y'+3=0$. (iv) $3x'^2+y'^2+\sqrt{2}(8x'+2y')+8=0$.

12. Take new origin at $(-1, 2)$.

Exercises on Chapter 4

page 56

1. $\left(\frac{1}{\sqrt{2}}, \frac{1}{\sqrt{2}}, 0\right)$ and $\left(\frac{1}{\sqrt{2}}, -\frac{1}{\sqrt{2}}, 0\right)$.

2. $\left(0, -\frac{1}{\sqrt{2}}, -\frac{1}{\sqrt{2}}\right)$ and $\left(\frac{4}{3\sqrt{2}}, \frac{1}{3\sqrt{2}}, \frac{1}{3\sqrt{2}}\right)$;

(1, 0, 0) and $\left(\frac{1}{3}, -\frac{2}{3}, -\frac{2}{3}\right)$.

3. $\left(\frac{-3+2\sqrt{2}}{6}, \frac{\sqrt{2}}{6}, \frac{3+2\sqrt{2}}{6}\right)$

and $\left(\frac{-3-2\sqrt{2}}{6}, -\frac{\sqrt{2}}{6}, \frac{3-2\sqrt{2}}{6}\right)$.

4. By the sine formula for the area, $4A^2=|\mathbf{a}|^2|\mathbf{b}|^2\sin^2\theta$ $=|\mathbf{a}|^2|\mathbf{b}|^2(1-\cos^2\theta)=|\mathbf{a}|^2|\mathbf{b}|^2-(\mathbf{a}.\mathbf{b})^2$.

5. Take A as origin. Then $\mathbf{b}.(\mathbf{c}-\mathbf{d})=\mathbf{c}.(\mathbf{d}-\mathbf{b})=0$, so

$$\mathbf{b}.\mathbf{c}=\mathbf{c}.\mathbf{d}=\mathbf{d}.\mathbf{b} \text{ and } \mathbf{d}.(\mathbf{b}-\mathbf{c})=0,$$

i.e., AD is perpendicular to BC.

6. Let **a**, **b** be the vector sides of the parallelogram. Then the vectors given by the diagonals are $\mathbf{a}\pm\mathbf{b}$. The result follows from the identity $|\mathbf{a}-\mathbf{b}|^2+|\mathbf{a}+\mathbf{b}|^2=2(|\mathbf{a}|^2+|\mathbf{b}|^2)$.

7. Let **O, a, b, c** be the position vectors of the vertices. The sum of the squares on the six edges is

$$\Sigma\,|\,\mathbf{a}\,|^2+\Sigma\,|\,\mathbf{b}-\mathbf{c}\,|^2 = 3\Sigma\,|\,\mathbf{a}\,|^2-2\Sigma\mathbf{b}.\mathbf{c},$$

while the sum of the squares on the segments joining the midpoints of opposite edges is $\frac{1}{4}\Sigma\,|\,\mathbf{a}-\mathbf{b}-\mathbf{c}\,|^2 = \frac{1}{4}(3\Sigma\,|\,\mathbf{a}\,|^2-2\Sigma\mathbf{b}.\mathbf{c})$.

8. The angle between OB and OC is 2A and their lengths are R. Hence $\overrightarrow{\mathrm{OB}}.\overrightarrow{\mathrm{OC}} = R^2\cos 2A$, $\overrightarrow{\mathrm{OC}}.\overrightarrow{\mathrm{OA}} = R^2\cos 2B$, $\overrightarrow{\mathrm{OA}}.\overrightarrow{\mathrm{OB}} = R^2\cos 2C$. Now (denoting $\overrightarrow{\mathrm{OA}}$ by **a** &c.) we have $bc\cos A = (\mathbf{b}-\mathbf{a}).(\mathbf{c}-\mathbf{a}) = |\,\mathbf{a}\,|^2-\mathbf{a}.\mathbf{b}-\mathbf{a}.\mathbf{c}+\mathbf{b}.\mathbf{c} = R^2(1-\cos 2B-\cos 2C+\cos 2A)$.

9. Using the notation of Chapter 2, § 8 and Q. 8 above,
$OH^2 = |\,\mathbf{a}+\mathbf{b}+\mathbf{c}\,|^2 = \Sigma\,|\,\mathbf{a}\,|^2+2\Sigma\mathbf{b}.\mathbf{c} = 3R^2+2R^2\,.\,\cos 2A$.

10.

$$k = \frac{(\mathbf{p}.\mathbf{a})\,|\,\mathbf{b}\,|^2-(\mathbf{p}.\mathbf{b})(\mathbf{a}.\mathbf{b})}{|\,\mathbf{a}\,|^2\,|\,\mathbf{b}\,|^2-(\mathbf{a}.\mathbf{b})^2},\quad l = \frac{(\mathbf{p}.\mathbf{b})\,|\,\mathbf{a}\,|^2-(\mathbf{p}.\mathbf{a})(\mathbf{a}.\mathbf{b})}{|\,\mathbf{a}\,|^2\,|\,\mathbf{b}\,|^2-(\mathbf{a}.\mathbf{b})^2}.$$

11. $\overrightarrow{\mathbf{CA}} = \mathbf{a}-\mathbf{c}$, $\overrightarrow{\mathbf{AB}} = \mathbf{b}-\mathbf{a}$, $\overrightarrow{\mathbf{OM}} = \frac{1}{2}(\mathbf{b}+\mathbf{c})$, $\overrightarrow{\mathbf{MA}} = \mathbf{a}-\frac{1}{2}(\mathbf{b}+\mathbf{c})$. **BAC** is a right angle if $0 = \overrightarrow{\mathrm{CA}}.\overrightarrow{\mathrm{AB}} = \mathbf{a}.\mathbf{b}+\mathbf{a}.\mathbf{c}-\mathbf{b}.\mathbf{c}-|\,\mathbf{a}\,|^2$, **OMA** is a right angle if

$$0 = \overrightarrow{\mathrm{OM}}.\overrightarrow{\mathrm{MA}} = \tfrac{1}{4}(2\mathbf{a}.(\mathbf{b}+\mathbf{c})+|\,\mathbf{b}\,|^2+|\,\mathbf{c}\,|^2-2\mathbf{b}.\mathbf{c}).$$

If we substitute 1 for $|\,\mathbf{a}\,|^2$, $|\,\mathbf{b}\,|^2$ $|\,\mathbf{c}\,|^2$, $\cos\alpha$ for $\mathbf{b}.\mathbf{c}$ &c., both these conditions reduce to the desired form.

12. (i) Number 8; (ii) vector (5, 7, 9); (iii) vector (4, 0, 4); (iv) number 45.

13. $\mathbf{AB} = \sqrt{38}$, $\mathbf{BC} = 3\sqrt{6}$, $\mathbf{CA} = \sqrt{10}$;

$$\cos A = \frac{-3}{2\sqrt{95}},\quad \cos B = \frac{41}{6\sqrt{57}},\quad \cos C = \frac{13}{6\sqrt{15}}.\quad \text{Area} = \tfrac{1}{2}\sqrt{371}.$$

14. If **u** and **v** are perpendicular, then

$$0 = \mathbf{u}.\mathbf{v} = (\mathbf{a}.\mathbf{c})\,|\,\mathbf{b}\,|^2-(\mathbf{b}.\mathbf{c})(\mathbf{c}.\mathbf{a})(\mathbf{a}.\mathbf{b}) = \cos^2\beta-\cos\alpha\cos\beta\cos\gamma.$$

15. If l denotes the common length of all the edges, we have

$$l^2 = |\,\mathbf{b}\,|^2 = |\,\mathbf{c}\,|^2 = |\,\mathbf{b}-\mathbf{c}\,|^2 = |\,\mathbf{b}\,|^2-2\mathbf{b}.\mathbf{c}+|\,\mathbf{c}\,|^2, \text{ so } 2\mathbf{b}.\mathbf{c} = l^2.$$

Hence

$$\overrightarrow{\mathbf{PA}}.\overrightarrow{\mathbf{PB}} = \left[\frac{1}{6}(\mathbf{a}+\mathbf{b}+\mathbf{c})-\mathbf{a}\right].\left[\frac{1}{6}(\mathbf{a}+\mathbf{b}+\mathbf{c})-\mathbf{b}\right]$$

$$= \frac{1}{36}(-5\,|\,\mathbf{a}\,|^2-5\,|\,\mathbf{b}\,|^2+\,|\,\mathbf{c}\,|^2-4\mathbf{b}.\mathbf{c}-4\mathbf{c}.\mathbf{a}+26\mathbf{a}.\mathbf{b})$$

$$= \frac{l^2}{36}(-5-5+1-2-2+13) = 0.$$

16. All four faces have area $9\sqrt{6}$.

Exercises on Chapter 5 page 72

2. The area is half the magnitude of the following vector product (Note 1, p. 61):

$$(\mathbf{b}-\mathbf{a})\times(\mathbf{c}-\mathbf{a}) = \mathbf{b}\times\mathbf{c}-\mathbf{b}\times\mathbf{a}-\mathbf{a}\times\mathbf{c}+\mathbf{a}\times\mathbf{a}$$
$$= \mathbf{b}\times\mathbf{c}+\mathbf{c}\times\mathbf{a}+\mathbf{a}\times\mathbf{b} \text{ (Note 2, p. 61).}$$

3. Since $\mathbf{a}\times\mathbf{a} = \mathbf{b}\times\mathbf{b} = \mathbf{0}$ and $\mathbf{b}\times\mathbf{a} = -(\mathbf{a}\times\mathbf{b})$,

$$(r\mathbf{a}+s\mathbf{b})\times(t\mathbf{a}+u\mathbf{b}) = rt\mathbf{0}-st(\mathbf{a}\times\mathbf{b})+ru(\mathbf{a}\times\mathbf{b})+su\mathbf{0}.$$

4. (a) If $\mathbf{v}$ is the projection of $\mathbf{x}$ on P then $\mathbf{x} = \mathbf{v}+k\mathbf{n}$, where k is a number and $\mathbf{v}.\mathbf{n} = 0$. Hence $\mathbf{x}.\mathbf{n} = \mathbf{v}.\mathbf{n}+k\,|\,\mathbf{n}\,|^2 = 0+k$, since $\mathbf{n}$ is a unit vector. Then $\mathbf{v} = \mathbf{x}-k\mathbf{n} = \mathbf{x}-(\mathbf{x}.\mathbf{n})\mathbf{n}$.

(b) Since $\mathbf{n}$ is a unit vector, the expansion E mentioned in § 5 will not occur when one takes a vector product with $\mathbf{n}$. Thus $\mathbf{n}\times\mathbf{x}$ will be the result of rotating the projection $\mathbf{v}$ through an angle of 90 degrees in the plane P. The vector $(\mathbf{x}.\mathbf{n})\mathbf{n}$, parallel to the axis of rotation, will be rotated into itself. Hence the vector $\mathbf{x} = \mathbf{v}+(\mathbf{x}.\mathbf{n})\mathbf{n}$ will be rotated into $\mathbf{n}\times\mathbf{x}+(\mathbf{x}.\mathbf{n})\mathbf{n}$.

5. Since the vector product $\mathbf{a}\times\mathbf{x}$ must be perpendicular to $\mathbf{a}$, there will be no vector $\mathbf{x}$ satisfying the equation unless $\mathbf{a}.\mathbf{b} = 0$. If $\mathbf{a}.\mathbf{b} = \mathbf{0}$, there will certainly be a vector $\mathbf{p}$ in the plane perpendicular to $\mathbf{b}$ with the property that the area of the parallelogram $(\mathbf{a}, \mathbf{p})$ is equal to $|\,\mathbf{b}\,|$. Then $\mathbf{a}\times\mathbf{p}$ will be $\pm\mathbf{b}$, since it agrees in magnitude and direction, though it may differ in sense. On changing $\mathbf{p}$ to $-\mathbf{p}$, if necessary, we may take it that $\mathbf{a}\times\mathbf{p} = \mathbf{b}$. If now $\mathbf{a}\times\mathbf{x} = \mathbf{b}$, it follows that $\mathbf{a}\times(\mathbf{x}-\mathbf{p}) = \mathbf{0}$, so that $\mathbf{x}-\mathbf{p}$ is parallel to $\mathbf{a}$. Thus the locus of all such $\mathbf{x}$ is the line through $\mathbf{p}$ parallel to $\mathbf{a}$.

6. (i) $(-10, 7, -16)$; (ii) $(-5, 0, 5)$; (iii) -20; (iv) -15; (v) 20.

8. Since $\mathbf{v}$ is a unit vector and $\mathbf{a}$ is at right angles to $\mathbf{v}$, it follows that $\mathbf{b} = \mathbf{v}\times\mathbf{a}$ is obtained by rotating $\mathbf{a}$ through a right angle about $\mathbf{v}$. Then $\mathbf{v}\times\mathbf{b}$ is the result of rotating $\mathbf{a}$ through *two* right angles, i.e., $\mathbf{v}\times\mathbf{b} = -\mathbf{a}$.

9. From $\mathbf{a}\times\mathbf{b} = \mathbf{c}$ it follows that $\mathbf{c}$ is at right angles to $\mathbf{a}$ and $\mathbf{b}$ and from $\mathbf{b}\times\mathbf{c} = \mathbf{a}$ it follows that $\mathbf{a}$ is at right angles to $\mathbf{b}$ and $\mathbf{c}$. Comparing magnitudes (with $\sin\theta = 1$), $|\mathbf{a}||\mathbf{b}| = |\mathbf{c}|$ and $|\mathbf{b}||\mathbf{c}| = |\mathbf{a}|$ so $|\mathbf{b}| = 1$, $|\mathbf{a}| = |\mathbf{c}|$. If also $\mathbf{c}\times\mathbf{a} = \mathbf{b}$, then $\mathbf{a}, \mathbf{b}, \mathbf{c}$ all have unit length.

10. $(\mathbf{a}-\mathbf{b})\times\mathbf{c} = \mathbf{0}$, so $\mathbf{a}-\mathbf{b} = k\mathbf{c}$. Hence $|\mathbf{a}|^2-\mathbf{a}.\mathbf{b} = k\mathbf{a}.\mathbf{c}$, i.e., $1-\mathbf{a}.\mathbf{b} = k/\sqrt{2}$, and $|\mathbf{a}|^2-2\mathbf{a}.\mathbf{b}+|\mathbf{b}|^2 = k^2|\mathbf{c}|^2$, $2-2\mathbf{a}.\mathbf{b} = k^2$. Thus $k^2 = k\sqrt{2}$, and since $\mathbf{a}$ and $\mathbf{b}$ are distinct, $k \neq 0$, so $k = \sqrt{2}$, and $\mathbf{a}.\mathbf{b} = 0$.

11. (a) Let $\mathbf{p}$ be the projection of $\mathbf{x}$ on the plane perpendicular to $\mathbf{v}$, let $\mathbf{x}'$ be the vector in its rotated position and $\mathbf{p}'$ the projection of $\mathbf{x}'$. As in Question 4b we have

$$\mathbf{x}' = \mathbf{p}'+(\mathbf{v}.\mathbf{x})\mathbf{v}$$
$$\mathbf{x} = \mathbf{p}+(\mathbf{v}.\mathbf{x})\mathbf{v}.$$

Also $\mathbf{v}\times\mathbf{x}$ lies in the plane perpendicular to $\mathbf{v}$ and is obtained from $\mathbf{p}$ by rotation through a right angle. From the diagram on the right

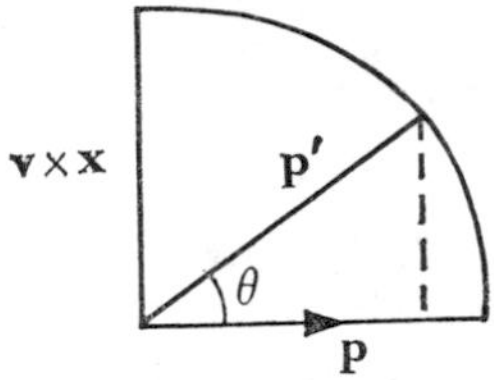

we derive the equation

$$\mathbf{p}' = \cos\theta\,\mathbf{p}+\sin\theta(\mathbf{v}\times\mathbf{x}).$$

Substituting for $\mathbf{p}$ and $\mathbf{p}'$ yields the required formula.

(b) The unit vector $\mathbf{v}$ with the same direction and sense as (2, 2, 1) is $\mathbf{v} = (\frac{2}{3}, \frac{2}{3}, \frac{1}{3})$. Taking this vector as $\mathbf{v}$ and θ as 45° in formula (a) we find $\mathbf{x}' = (10+\sqrt{2}, 10-2\sqrt{2}, 5+2\sqrt{2})$.

12. $\mathbf{c}.\mathbf{a} = p+\frac{1}{2}q$, $\mathbf{c}.\mathbf{b} = \frac{1}{2}p+q$, $p = \frac{2}{3}$, $q = -\frac{1}{3}$, $r = \pm\dfrac{2\sqrt{2}}{3}$.

Exercises page 79

1. (i) Non-collinear, $y-z = 3$; (ii) collinear; (iii) non-collinear, $x+y = 9$.

2. If a plane contains the points A, B, C its normal vector (p, q, r) must be perpendicular to the vector $\overrightarrow{AB} = (-1, 1, -1)$, so $-p+q-r = 0$. The most general solution is $r = k$, $q = l$, $p = k-l$. The equation of the plane takes the form

$$(k-l)x+ly-kz = t.$$

The condition that B should lie on the plane yields $t = 3l-2k$.

Exercises 6.1 page 90

1. $2x+z = 3$.

2. Sides $\sqrt{6}$, $\sqrt{6}$, $\sqrt{22}$; cosines of angles $\dfrac{11}{2\sqrt{33}}, \dfrac{5}{6}, \dfrac{11}{2\sqrt{33}}$; area $\frac{1}{2}\sqrt{11}$; plane $x+3y+z = 2$. Sides $\sqrt{6}$, $2\sqrt{11}$, $\sqrt{42}$; cosines of angles $\dfrac{1}{3\sqrt{7}}, \dfrac{2}{\sqrt{66}}, \dfrac{20}{\sqrt{462}}$; area $\sqrt{62}$; plane $3x+7y+2z = 8$.

3. Area $\frac{1}{2}\sqrt{3}$; perpendicular distance $1/\sqrt{3}$.

4. $4x+3y-z = 1$; $(\frac{23}{13}, -\frac{12}{13}, \frac{43}{13})$.

5. (i) Sides 3, $\sqrt{6}$, $\sqrt{3}$; cosines of angles $0, \dfrac{1}{\sqrt{3}}, \dfrac{\sqrt{2}}{\sqrt{3}}$; foot of perpendicular $(-\frac{3}{2}, 0, \frac{3}{2})$. (ii) Sides $\sqrt{2}$, $\sqrt{14}$, $\sqrt{14}$; cosines of angles $\dfrac{1}{2\sqrt{7}}, \dfrac{1}{2\sqrt{7}}, \dfrac{13}{14}$; foot of perpendicular $(-\frac{1}{9}, -\frac{1}{9}, \frac{5}{9})$.

6. $3/\sqrt{455}$.

7. The given equation represents a plane and it is satisfied by the coordinates of the points given. Let $(a', 0, 0)$ &c. be the coordinates of the points A$'$, B$'$, C$'$. Then G$'$ is $(\frac{1}{3}a', \frac{1}{3}b', \frac{1}{3}c')$ and the normal vector of the plane ABC is $\left(\dfrac{1}{a}, \dfrac{1}{b}, \dfrac{1}{c}\right)$. For these to be parallel, we must have $aa' = bb' = cc'$. The symmetry of this condition proves the result.

8. $(1, 4, -9)$.

10. $\dfrac{x-3}{5} = -\dfrac{y-5}{7} = \dfrac{z-2}{4}$. $(\frac{32}{9}, \frac{38}{9}, \frac{22}{9})$.

11. $5x+6y-7z = 12$.

12. $\frac{5}{9}$. $(\frac{26}{27}, \frac{5}{27}, \frac{1}{27})$.

13. Follows from symmetry. The sides of the triangle are permuted by cyclic interchange of x, y, z, so they have the same length.

14. (i) $\dfrac{1}{\sqrt{14}}(1, 3, -2)$; $x = t+3\frac{1}{2}$, $y = 3t-1\frac{1}{2}$, $z = -2t$.

(ii) $\dfrac{1}{\sqrt{89}}(4, 8, -3)$; $x = 4t+\frac{4}{3}$, $y = 8t-\frac{1}{3}$, $z = -3t$.

(iii) $\dfrac{1}{\sqrt{2}}(1, 1, 0)$; $x = t+\frac{17}{5}$, $y = t$, $z = \frac{3}{5}$.

15. $30°$.

16. $\dfrac{x-1}{2} = \dfrac{y-6}{-1} = z$; $(1, 6, 0)$.

Exercises 6.2 page 104

1. $\dfrac{13}{2\sqrt{105}}$.

2. $(1, 1, 1)$ and $(2, 1, 0)$.

3. $x+4y-z = 0$.

4. $\dfrac{x+3}{-1} = \dfrac{y+2}{1} = \dfrac{z-7}{1}$.

5. $\cos^{-1}\dfrac{17}{5\sqrt{13}}$; $x-4y+3z = 15$.

6. $y-z = 1$.

7. $x-y-z = 0$; $\dfrac{1}{\sqrt{3}}$.

8. $(1, 1, 1)$.

9. $x+y-z = 2$; $x+y-z = -1$; $\sqrt{3}$.

10. $\cos^{-1}\sqrt{\dfrac{2}{11}}$.

11. $x+y-z = 3$; $\sqrt{3}$.

12. (i) $5x-3y-z = -3$; (ii) $5x-3y-z = -7$; (iii) $x \quad 2z = 0$; (v) $y-3z = 1$; (v) $5x+11y-8z = 49$.

13. $x+2 = \dfrac{y+2}{2} = \dfrac{z+2}{-3}$.

14. $\dfrac{6x-2}{13} = \dfrac{y-1}{3} = \dfrac{z-1}{-2}$.

15. $x+y = 6$ and $x+4y+z = 6$.

16. $\dfrac{x}{4} = \dfrac{y}{13} = \dfrac{z}{2}$.

Exercises page 108

1. $7x'^2+10y'^2+z'^2+11x'y'-z'x'+8x'y' = 9$.

3. In equations (5) put $x_1 = 1$, $x_2 = x_3 = 0$. We find $x_1' = l_1$, $x_2' = l_2$, $x_3' = l_3$. Substitute these values back into equations (4) to obtain the result.

4. $\mathbf{u}_2 = (\frac{3}{7}, -\frac{2}{7}, -\frac{6}{7})$, $\mathbf{u}_3 = (-\frac{2}{7}, \frac{6}{7}, -\frac{3}{7})$.

Exercises page 110

1. $\mathbf{q}\times\mathbf{r} = (\mathbf{c}\times\mathbf{a})\times\mathbf{r} = (\mathbf{c}.\mathbf{r})\mathbf{a}-(\mathbf{a}.\mathbf{r})\mathbf{c} = [\mathbf{a}, \mathbf{b}, \mathbf{c}]\mathbf{a}$, since $\mathbf{a}.\mathbf{r} = 0$. Thus $\mathbf{p}.(\mathbf{q}\times\mathbf{r}) = [\mathbf{a}, \mathbf{b}, \mathbf{c}](\mathbf{a}.\mathbf{p}) = [\mathbf{a}, \mathbf{b}, \mathbf{c}]^2$. If $\mathbf{p}, \mathbf{q}, \mathbf{r}$ are known, then $\mathbf{a}, \mathbf{b}, \mathbf{c}$ is now determined apart from sign, and $\mathbf{a}$ is given by the formula $\mathbf{a} = \mathbf{q}\times\mathbf{r}/[\mathbf{a}, \mathbf{b}, \mathbf{c}]$.

2. From $\mathbf{p}+\mathbf{q}+\mathbf{r}+\mathbf{s} = \mathbf{0}$ follows
$|\mathbf{p}|^2+|\mathbf{q}|^2+2\mathbf{p}.\mathbf{q} = |\mathbf{p}+\mathbf{q}|^2 = |-(\mathbf{r}+\mathbf{s})|^2 = |\mathbf{r}|^2+|\mathbf{s}|^2+2\mathbf{r}.\mathbf{s}$.
Hence $\mathbf{p}.\mathbf{q} = \mathbf{r}.\mathbf{s}$, $|\mathbf{p}\times\mathbf{q}|^2 = |\mathbf{p}|^2|\mathbf{q}|^2-(\mathbf{p}.\mathbf{q})^2$
$$= |\mathbf{r}|^2|\mathbf{s}|^2-(\mathbf{r}.\mathbf{s})^2 = |\mathbf{r}\times\mathbf{s}|^2$$

3. As in Question 1, let $\mathbf{p} = \mathbf{b}\times\mathbf{c}$ &c., and put $\mathbf{s} = (\mathbf{a}-\mathbf{b})\times(\mathbf{c}-\mathbf{a})$. Then $\mathbf{p}+\mathbf{q}+\mathbf{r}+\mathbf{s} = \mathbf{0}$, so by Q.2 $|\mathbf{p}\times\mathbf{q}| = |\mathbf{r}\times\mathbf{s}|$, i.e.,
$$|[\mathbf{a}, \mathbf{b}, \mathbf{c}]\,\mathbf{a}| = |[\mathbf{a}, \mathbf{b}, \mathbf{c}](\mathbf{b}-\mathbf{c})|.$$
In the tetrahedron OABC, $\mathbf{p}, \mathbf{q}, \mathbf{r}, \mathbf{s}$ are twice the vector areas of the faces, and $\mathbf{a}, \mathbf{b}-\mathbf{c}$ define opposite edges.

4. Put $\mathbf{y} = \mathbf{a}\times\mathbf{b}$. Then $(\mathbf{a}\times\mathbf{b}).(\mathbf{c}\times\mathbf{d}) = \mathbf{y}.(\mathbf{c}\times\mathbf{d}) = (\mathbf{y}\times\mathbf{c}).\mathbf{d}$.
Now $\mathbf{y}\times\mathbf{c} = (\mathbf{a}\times\mathbf{b})\times\mathbf{c} = (\mathbf{a}.\mathbf{c})\mathbf{b}-(\mathbf{a}.\mathbf{b})\mathbf{c}$.
Hence $(\mathbf{y}\times\mathbf{c}).\mathbf{d} = (\mathbf{a}.\mathbf{c})(\mathbf{b}.\mathbf{d})-(\mathbf{a}.\mathbf{b})(\mathbf{c}.\mathbf{d})$.

5. (i) is the vector triple product formula for $\mathbf{r}\times(\mathbf{c}\times\mathbf{d})$ with $\mathbf{r} = \mathbf{a}\times\mathbf{b}$; (ii) is the same for $(\mathbf{a}\times\mathbf{b})\times\mathbf{s}$ with $\mathbf{s} = \mathbf{c}\times\mathbf{d}$. The second part follows either by equating these expressions, or by expanding each term using (7), obtaining twelve terms which cancel in pairs because of the anticommutativity $\mathbf{a}\times\mathbf{b} = -\mathbf{b}\times\mathbf{a}$.

Exercises on spherical trigonometry page 118

2. $\sin^2 b \sin^2 c \sin^2 A = \sin^2 b \sin^2 c-\sin^2 b \sin^2 c \cos^2 A$
$= \sin^2 b \sin^2 c-(\cos a-\cos b \cos c)^2$, by the cosine rule,
$= \{\cos (b-c)-\cos a\}\{\cos a-\cos (b+c)\}$
$= 4 \sin s \sin (s-a) \sin (s-b) \sin (s-c)$, where $2s = a+b+c$.
The sine rule follows from the symmetry of the above expression.

3. Put $b = c = a$ in the cosine rule to obtain
$\cos a = \cos^2 a+\sin^2 a \cos A$, so $\cos a\,(1-\cos a) = (1-\cos^2 a) \cos A$.

Dividing across by $1-\cos a$, which is not zero because $a \neq 0$, the result follows. The second equation follows on putting $\cos a = 2\cos^2 \frac{1}{2}a - 1$, $\cos A = 1 - 2\sin^2 \frac{1}{2}A$.

4.

$$\cos^2 \tfrac{1}{2}A = \tfrac{1}{2}(1+\cos A) = \frac{\sin b \sin c + \cos a - \cos b \cos c}{2 \sin b \sin c}$$

$$= \frac{\cos a - \cos (b+c)}{2 \sin b \sin c} \qquad = \frac{2 \sin s \sin (s-a)}{2 \sin b \sin c}.$$

The formula for $\sin^2 \frac{1}{2}A$ follows by a similar argument, and that for $\tan^2 \frac{1}{2}A$ is obtained by division.

5. (i) Put $\cos C = 0$ in the cosine rule:

$$\cos c = \cos a \cos b + \sin a \sin b \cos C.$$

(iii) Put $\sin C = 1$ in the sine rule: $\sin C \sin a = \sin A \sin c$. (v) Put $\cos C = 0$, $\sin C = 1$ in the cosine rule for the polar triangle:

$$\cos A = -\cos B \cos C + \sin B \sin C \cos a.$$

(ii) By (i), (iii), $\cos A = \sin B \cos a = \dfrac{\sin b}{\sin c} \cdot \dfrac{\cos c}{\cos b}$. (iv) Multiply the left side of (i) and (ii) by the right side of (iii), equate to the right side of (i) and (ii) multiplied with the left side of (iii) and simplify.

6. The vector $\mathbf{b} \times \mathbf{c}$ has magnitude $\sin A$ and direction perpendicular to the plane BOC. The angle between $\mathbf{a}$ and $\mathbf{b} \times \mathbf{c}$ is therefore $\dfrac{\pi}{2} - \alpha$. We have

$$\sin a \sin \alpha = [\mathbf{a}, \mathbf{b}, \mathbf{c}] = \sin b \sin c \sin A \text{ (p. 115)}.$$

Also $\sin a \cos \alpha$ is the magnitude of the vector

$$\mathbf{a} \times (\mathbf{b} \times \mathbf{c}) = (\mathbf{a}.\mathbf{c})\mathbf{b} - (\mathbf{a}.\mathbf{b})\mathbf{c}.$$

Hence $\sin^2 a \cos^2 \alpha = (\mathbf{a}.\mathbf{c})^2 |\,\mathbf{b}\,|^2 + (\mathbf{a}.\mathbf{b})^2 |\,\mathbf{c}\,|^2 - 2(\mathbf{b}.\mathbf{c})(\mathbf{c}.\mathbf{a})(\mathbf{a}.\mathbf{b})$.
$= \cos^2 b + \cos^2 c - 2 \cos a \cos b \cos c$.

Exercises on the tetrahedron page 122

1. By the distance formula, every edge has length $a\sqrt{2}$, so the tetrahedron is regular. Volume = scalar triple product of vector edges $= \frac{1}{3}a^3$, shortest distance $= a$. These results reduce to those in the text on replacing a by $l/\sqrt{2}$.

2. Volume $\frac{5}{12}\sqrt{95}$; shortest distances: AB to CD $\frac{1}{8}\sqrt{95}$, AC to BD $\frac{5}{8}\sqrt{19}$, AD to BC $\frac{5}{8}\sqrt{19}$.

3. If **0**, **a**, **b**, **c** are the position vectors of the vertices, then $l = |\mathbf{a}|$, $l' = |\mathbf{b}-\mathbf{c}|$;

$$\begin{aligned} 2ll' \cos\theta &= 2\mathbf{a}.(\mathbf{b}-\mathbf{c}) \\ &= |\mathbf{b}|^2 + |\mathbf{a}-\mathbf{c}|^2 - |\mathbf{c}|^2 - |\mathbf{a}-\mathbf{b}|^2 \\ &= m^2+m'^2-(n^2+n'^2). \end{aligned}$$

4. Since $|\mathbf{x}|^2 = |\mathbf{x}-\mathbf{a}|^2 = |\mathbf{x}|^2 + |\mathbf{a}|^2 - 2\mathbf{x}.\mathbf{a}$, we have $\mathbf{x}.\mathbf{a} = \frac{1}{2}|\mathbf{a}|^2$ and two similar equations. Now apply formula (7), p. 109 with **b** replaced by **x**, **c** and **d** replaced by **b**, **c**.

Exercises on the cube page 124

3. 12 (two for each of six faces); 4 (joining the eight vertices in pairs).

4. 6 (three meet it at each of its two endpoints); 6 ($= 12-6$).

6. An edge joins two vertices, and the *opposite* edge joins the two opposite vertices. Opposite edges are parallel.

7. 2, 5, 1, 5.

9. (i) $2a$, (ii) $\dfrac{2a}{\sqrt{3}}$.

10. If P Q are the adjacent vertices, the other vertices are obtained by rotating through $\pm 90°$ and $180°$ about an axis parallel to PQ through the origin. Use the formula of Ex. 4b, p. 73 to obtain

$(5, -1, -1)$ $(-5, 1, 1)$, $(3, 3, 3)$, $(-3, -3, -3)$
$(1, 1, -5)$, $(-1, -1, 5)$, $(1, -5, 1)$, $(-1, 5, -1)$.

INDEX